SCHOLASTIC

Traits Writing™

Student Handbook

Credits

Cover: bl: © 81a/Alamy, tl: © Image Source/Getty Images, r: © Dmitry Rukhlenko/Shutterstock; p. 39: © Juan Monino/iStockphoto; p. 47: © Atlanta Journal Constitution/AP Images; p. 55: © Sergei Bachlakov/Shutterstock; p. 65: © Sherri R. Camp/Shutterstock; p. 73: © Friedrich Stark/Alamy; p. 81: © Glow Images/SuperStock; p. 91: © Sindre Ellingsen/Getty Images; p. 99: © Comstock/Getty Images; p. 107: © Andersen Ross/Blend Images; p. 117: © Elena Aliaga/Shutterstock; p. 125: © Freeze Frame Studio/iStockphoto; p. 133: © Jack Hollingsworth/Monsoon/Photolibrary/Corbis; p. 143 l: © Jose Luis Pelaez Inc/Blend Images, r: © Bruce Laurance/Blend Images; p. 151: © JGI/Blend Images; p. 159: © 81a/Alamy; p. 169 l: © Jose Luis Pelaez/Blend/MediaBakery; tr: © Juriah Mosin/Shutterstock; br: © Divine/MediaBakery; p. 177: © Meg Takamura/Getty Images; p. 185: © Dianne Humble/AP Images; p. 195 boy: © Media Bakery/MediaBakery; well: © Hola Images/age fotostock; p. 203: © Bosenok/iStockphoto; p. 211: © Dimitri Vervitsiotis/Getty Images

Trait Mates illustration: Wook Jin Jung

Contents

Week 1
The Writing Process

Week 2
Prewriting
Focus Traits
Ideas, Organization, and Voice

Week 3
Drafting
Focus Traits
Word Choice and Sentence Fluency

Week 4
Revising
Focus Traits
Ideas, Organization, Voice, Word Choice, and Sentence Fluency

Week 5
Editing
Focus Traits
Conventions and Presentation

Getting Started

The writing traits are the language you use with your teacher and classmates to talk about what good writing looks like. The traits are

- **Ideas**
- **Organization**
- **Voice**
- **Word Choice**
- **Sentence Fluency**
- **Conventions**
- **Presentation**

You'll learn more about each trait in the weeks to come. You'll also learn how to use the traits in your own writing as you prewrite, draft, revise, edit, and publish. What makes the traits so great? They help YOU be a great writer!

Steps in the Writing Process

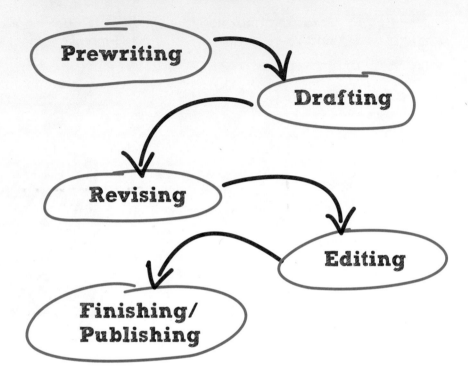

The Writing Process and the Writing Traits

Think of the writing process as steps that lead to choices you make as a writer. You can spend a lot of time on each one or just a little. You can follow them in order or go back to one to create a better piece.

When you use the writing process, you talk and think about your writing. That's where the traits come in. The traits are the words you use to describe good writing and qualities you check in your writing to make sure it is the best it can be. The writing process and the traits go hand in hand.

The Writing Process and Me

In the boxes below, fill in what's easy for you about writing and what's hard. If you need more space, continue on the bottom of the page.

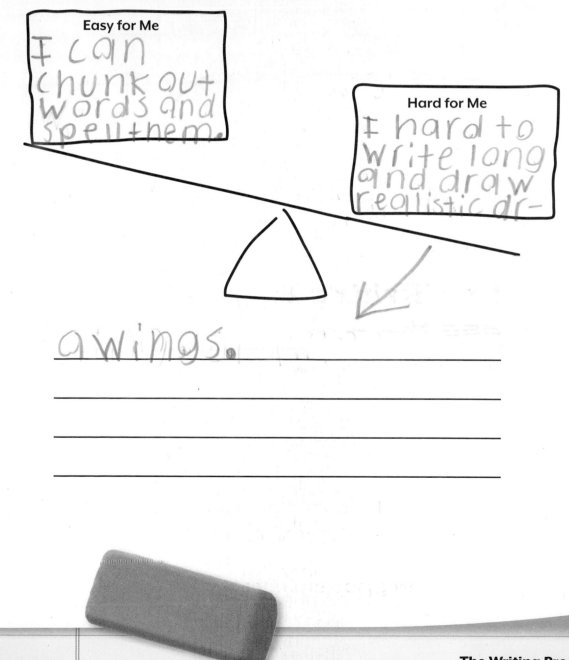

Easy for Me

I can chunk out words and spell them.

Hard for Me

I hard to write long and draw realistic dr-

awings.

The Writing Process

Meet the Trait Mates

List a few things you learned about each trait.

_____

_____

_____

_____

_____

_____

_____

_____

_____

_____

_____

_____

_____

_____

_____

_____

_____

_____

_____

_____

_____

Who I Am

What makes you the person you are? Write about it in the space below.

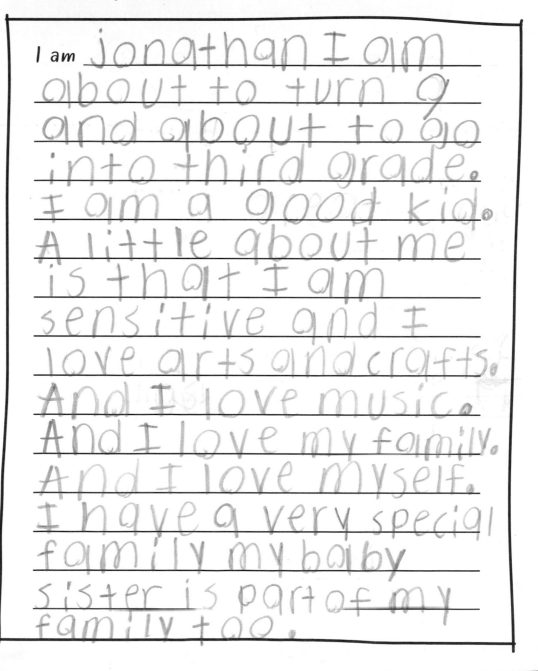

I am Jonathan I am
about to turn 9
and about to go
into third grade.
I am a good kid.
A little about me
is that I am
sensitive and I
love arts and crafts.
And I love music.
And I love my family.
And I love myself.
I have a very special
family my baby
sister is part of my
family too.

What Makes Me Unique

In *Looking Like Me,* Walter Dean Myers explains things that make Jeremy Jeremy. Now it's your turn. In the shapes below, explain things that make you you!

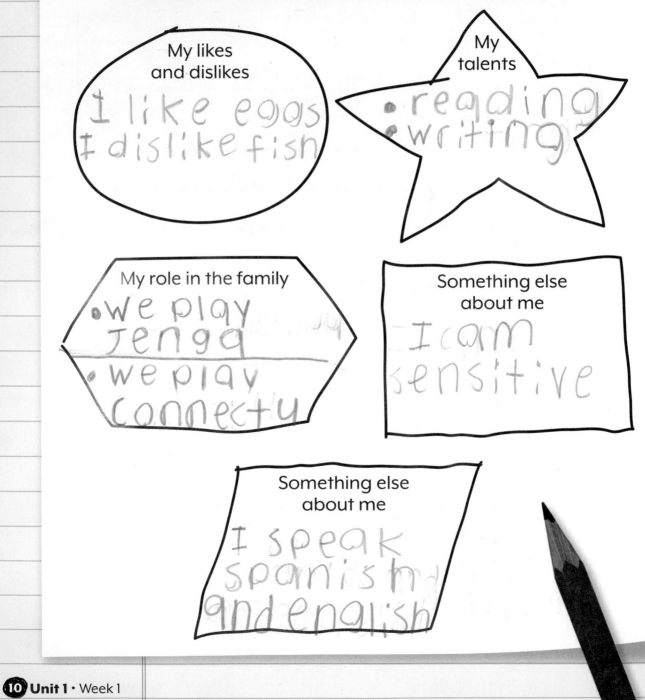

My likes and dislikes

I like eggs
I dislike fish

My talents

• reading
• writing

My role in the family

• we play Jenga
• we play connecty

Something else about me

I cam sensitive

Something else about me

I speak spanish andenglish

My Writing Goals

As I learn more about writing, I want to _____

_____

_____

_____

_____

_____

_____

_____

_____

_____

All right! Let's write!

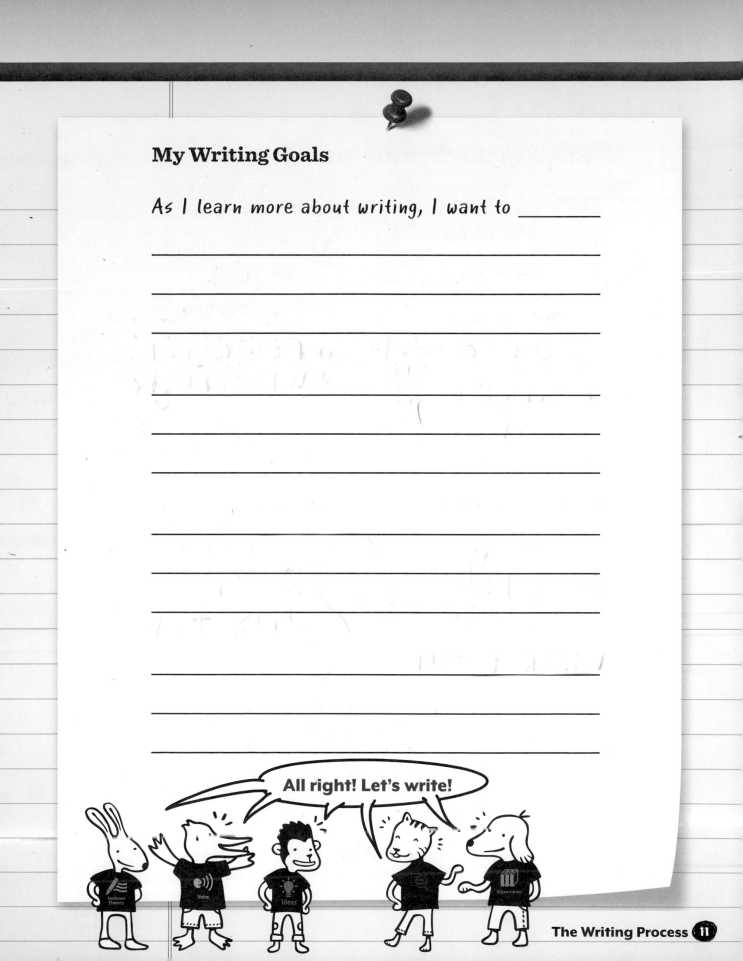

Steps in the Writing Process

Prewriting → Drafting → Revising → Editing → Finishing/Publishing

Prewriting

When you prewrite, you decide on the purpose and main topic for your writing. You also think about how to organize your ideas and how your piece should sound. Prewriting allows you to explore the possibilities and gives you a place to begin.

Okay, brains. Start your engines!

What Writers Think About As They Prewrite

Here are six techniques for prewriting and examples of what a writer might think about when applying them.

Sources for Ideas	Examples
Read Read books, magazines, and information on safe Internet sites.	Something interesting I read about is _____
Journal Write down your wonderings and experiences and use them in your writing.	Something I wonder about is _____
Talk Talk about topics with other writers; ask questions; talk to experts.	Here's a question I have for an expert. _____
Use Sensory Details Think about what you feel, see, smell, hear, and taste.	At the parade I... feel _____ see _____ smell _____ hear _____ taste _____
Create a Character Record things about interesting people you have seen, met, or read about.	Interesting people I know about: 1. 2. 3.
Listen as a Writer Listen to people, places, and things with a "writer's ear."	I overheard someone say _____

Prewriting Graphic Organizer

Choose a topic that interests you. Write that topic in the middle circle below. Then write main ideas about the topic in the rectangles, and supporting details in the ovals.

My Dream Room

Write about the bedroom of your dreams.
Draw a picture of what it might look like, too.

Prewriting

One Good Way to Prewrite

Choose a prewriting technique. Then explain how you would use that technique to write a piece about your family.

I will use this prewriting technique to write about my family.

☐ Reading ☐ Journaling ☐ Talking

☐ Using Sensory Details ☐ Creating a Character ☐ Listening as a Writer

This is how I will use this technique to prewrite about my family.

_____

_____

_____

_____

_____

_____

_____

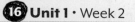

[Think About: **Prewriting**]

☐ Did I read, journal, talk, use sensory details, create a character, or listen as a writer to gather ideas for my topic?

☐ Did I think about my audience and my purpose for my writing?

☐ Did I begin to think about the best way to organize my ideas?

Notes About **Prewriting**

_____

_____

_____

_____

_____

_____

_____

Steps in the Writing Process

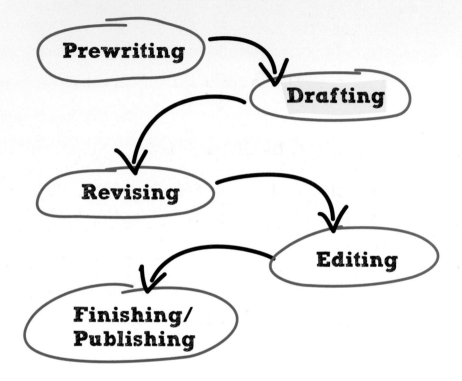

Prewriting → Drafting → Revising → Editing → Finishing/ Publishing

Drafting

You've come up with some original and intriguing ideas in prewriting. Now it's time to start drafting. When you draft, you get your ideas down in rough form. You put pencil to paper and let your ideas flow, not worrying about spelling or other conventions.

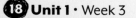

What Writers Do When They Draft

- Jump in and start writing!
- Get your ideas down on paper.
- Don't try to be perfect!
- Say to yourself, "I can come back and make it better!"

A Really Great Pet

Do you want a pet that is really, really big. Do you want a pet that is really gentle, too? Get Great Dane.

A Great Dane is tall. It is so tall, it can eat off a kitchen tabel. But dont let it!

A Great Dane have a short coat. It's easy to care for. But it needs lots of exercise. You might be really happy with a great Dane!

This draft is a dog!

Yes, it's rough, rough, rough, rough, rough!

Drafting

What's Difficult and Easy for Me When I Draft

Two things that slow me down when I draft are...

1. _____

_____

_____

2. _____

_____

_____

But two things that are easy for me when I draft are...

1. _____

_____

_____

2. _____

_____

_____

The Heart of a Hero

Write about what it means to be a hero.

Is your heart filled with *spectacular* WORD CHOICES?

My Everyday Hero: A 25-Word Sentence
Write a 25-word sentence about an everyday hero.

_____ _____ _____

_____ _____ (5)

_____ _____ _____

_____ _____ (10)

_____ _____ _____

_____ _____ (15)

_____ _____ _____

_____ _____ (20)

_____ _____ _____

_____ _____ . (25)

[Think About: **Drafting**]

☐ Did I use my prewriting ideas to write the lead, body, and ending of my piece?

☐ Did I just write, without worrying about making the piece perfect?

☐ Did I get interesting words and sentences down, knowing that I can revise them later?

My 7-Word Sentence

**Revise the 25-word sentence you drafted.
Make it a 7-word sentence.**

_____ _____ _____ _____

_____ _____ _____

Steps in the Writing Process

Revising

When you revise, you make changes to your writing so it is as clear as it can be. You reread your draft and rework it until it is just right for the reader. Save any worries about Conventions until the editing stage. Revising often begins with sharing your writing with someone else. Then you can use the traits to polish it up and make it shine!

What Writers Think About As They Revise

Here are some trait-based questions you can ask yourself when you revise.

Ideas

- Is my topic focused and developed?
- Does my piece contain specific, interesting, and accurate details?
- Have I included some new thinking about the topic?

Organization

- Do my details unfold in a logical order?
- Does the structure make reading my piece a breeze?

Voice

- Do I offer my own "take" on the topic?
- Do I have my audience and purpose clearly in mind?
- Do I present my ideas in an original way?

Word Choice

- Are my words and phrases accurate, specific, and natural-sounding?
- Do my words show that I have a powerful vocabulary?

Sentence Fluency

- Have I presented a variety of well-built sentences?

Great Dane, Great Pet

These sentences have no pizzazz. Revise them to make them more lively. Add sentences, if you wish.

1. A Great Dane is a big dog.

_____

_____

2. The dog ate his bowl of food.

_____

_____

3. The cat jumped on the table.

_____

_____

4. The horse ran into the barn.

_____

_____

5. The snake got out of its cage.

_____

_____

When I revise, I can make my writing stronger by . . .

_____

My Amazing, Marvelous, Wonderful, Awesome Name

Give yourself a special name, as Sophie does in *Sophie the Awesome*. Then write about what you need to do to live up to that name.

My name is _____

_____

_____

_____

To live up to my name, I need to _____

_____

_____

_____

_____

_____

Organization

Step aside! Someone **AWESOME** is about to write!

Revising

Even Great Writers Revise: E. B. White

Record examples of E. B. White's revisions to *Charlotte's Web.*

Revising for Word Choice

Draft	Revision

Revising for Sentence Fluency

Draft	Revision

[Think About: **Revising**]

- [ ] Did I zero in on a small part of my big idea?

- [ ] Did I anticipate and answer the reader's questions?

- [ ] Did I refine the words and sentences so they are clear?

- [ ] Did I start out strong and end just as strong?

Steps in the Writing Process

Editing

You edit because you want your reader to have no problem reading what you've written. When you edit, you check your work for spelling, capitalization, punctuation and paragraphing, and grammar and usage. You clean up your writing to follow the rules of standard English. Editing makes your work in all the other traits shine.

What Writers Think About As They Edit

Conventions are the "rules of the writing road"—spelling, capitalization, punctuation and paragraphing, and grammar and usage. They make your writing easy to read. They also help guide the reader through your writing. Here are some questions to ask yourself as you edit for conventions.

Spelling

• Did I spell words correctly—even the hard ones?

Capitalization

• Did I use capital letters correctly, even in tricky places?

Punctuation and Paragraphing

• Did I use punctuation correctly?
• Did I begin paragraphs in all the right places?

Grammar and Usage

• Did I follow grammar and usage rules?

Editing

The Editor's Chair

What needs to be corrected here? Use the editing marks on page 36 to improve this page.

A great Pet

Do you want a pet that is really big. Do you want a pet that is gentle, too? If you do, you shuld get a Great Dane. A Great Dane make a great pet!

A Great Dane can be 30 inches tall at the shoulders—that's tall enough to nibble food off your kitchen tabel. But dont let it!

A Great Dane have a short coat, so it's easy to groom. But a Great Dane still needs care. It needs lots of exercise. It needs you're love, too.

If you want the perfect big pet, get a great Dane. Youll have a great dog that grab everyone's attention!

[Think About: **Editing**]

☐ Did I check my spelling one word at a time?

☐ Did I use capital letters correctly?

☐ Did I add punctuation where it's needed?

☐ Did I indent all my paragraphs?

☐ Did I follow grammar and usage rules?

Tips for Editing on a Computer

Tools I Use to Edit for Conventions

insert	Add letters, words, phrases, or sentences.
delete	Remove letters, words, phrases, or sentences.
cut, copy, and paste	Highlight text to cut or copy it. This text can be pasted elsewhere.
check spelling	Have the computer underline possible misspelled words in red. Always double-check what the computer shows.

Tools I Use to Edit for Presentation

change font	Some fonts are easier to read than others. Select the best font for your document. You can even choose a fancy font for your title.
change style	You can <u>underline</u> text or make it **bold** or *italic*. You can also change the size of a word or make lowercase letters all UPPERCASE. If you have a list, you can use bullets (•) to make it easier to read.
change color	You can call attention to words using color.
insert art or graphics	Want to add a picture or chart to your document? Use clip art or a computer-generated graph.

I like your style.

Presentation

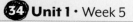

Rate the Papers

Read these two pieces written by third graders. Which piece is stronger, and why?

Sample 1

The best year was 1st grade. I had the nicest teacher in the world. She let us have guinea pigs. Guinea pigs are very fun. They can do tricks and are sneaky, too. Sometimes our guinea pigs got out and we had to look hard to find them. They make funny noises that always made me laugh. I met good friends in 1st grade and we did many fun things.

Sample 2

Out of all the years I have been in school, 1st grade was my favorite grade. We always had something fun to do. Everything was great.

For the first few days I was new to school, so I didn't know my way around too well. I did know immediately that I had one of the most desirable teachers possible. I learned to love our class schedule as much as school. Silent reading was (and still is) one of my favorite subjects. We had it for up to 45 minutes, which I particularly enjoyed. I also enjoyed that every day we had sharing. We brought something in to talk about in class. It was always fun to see what others brought and to bring in things of your own.

After a few weeks that were as wonderful as anyone could imagine, the weeks to follow only got better! We now had two cute walking fur balls around the classroom. I never knew guinea pigs could be so much fun! With their long nails on the hard floor they made a clicking noise, so we always knew where they were.

About the same time, I met my one of my best friends, Jack. I loved every moment of school now! Later in the year I met my other best friend, Sam. Both Jack and Sam are still my best friends today.

1st grade was my favorite year so far and I hope 3rd grade is even better!

Editing

Editing Marks

Mark	Meaning	Example
ℇ	Delete material.	The writing is is good.
sp	Correct the spelling or spell it out.	We are exploring ②traits this (weak). sp week
∩	Close space.	To day is publishing day.
∧	Insert a letter, word, or phrase.	My teacher has books. wonderful
✗	Change a letter.	She is a great wrîter.
⩘	Add a space.	Don't forget astrong lead.
∿	Transpose letters or words.	She raed the piece with flair!
≡	Change to a capital letter.	We have j. k. Rowling to thank for Harry Potter's magic.
/	Change to a lowercase letter.	"A Writer's work is never Done" was his favorite saying.
¶	Start a new paragraph	"What day is it?" he inquired. ¶"It's National Writing Day," she replied.
⊙	Add a period.	Think about all the traits as you write ⊙

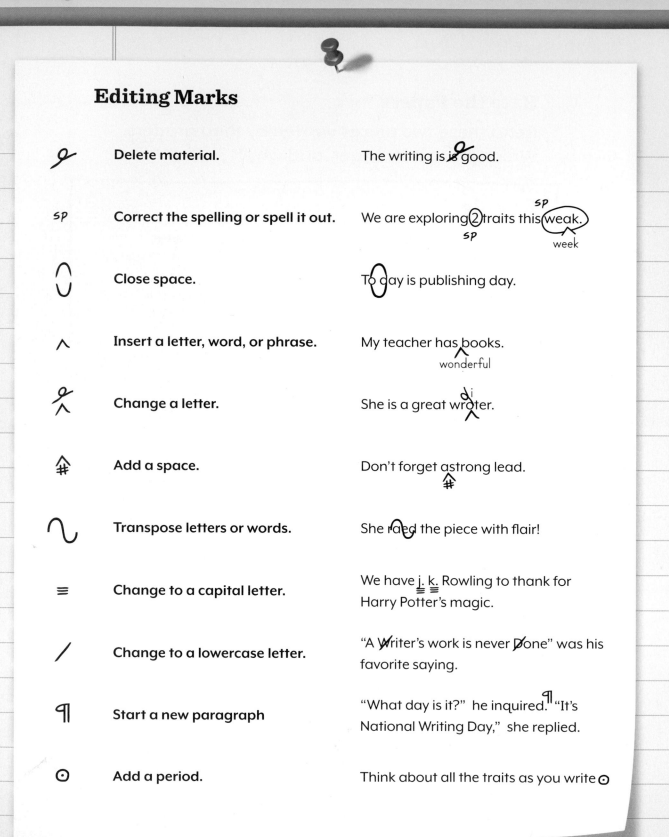

Focus Mode: Expository

Whether your topic is beetles, Bolivia, or bungee jumping, the main purpose of expository writing is to inform or explain. That said, your piece does not need to be just a bunch of facts—actually, it should not be! Think about including fascinating details, intriguing insights, and life experiences. Good expository writing is written in a strong, confident voice—a voice that tells the reader you know what you're talking about.

- **Finding a Topic** ······················
- Focusing the Topic
- Developing the Topic
- Using Details

Focus Mode: Expository

Ideas

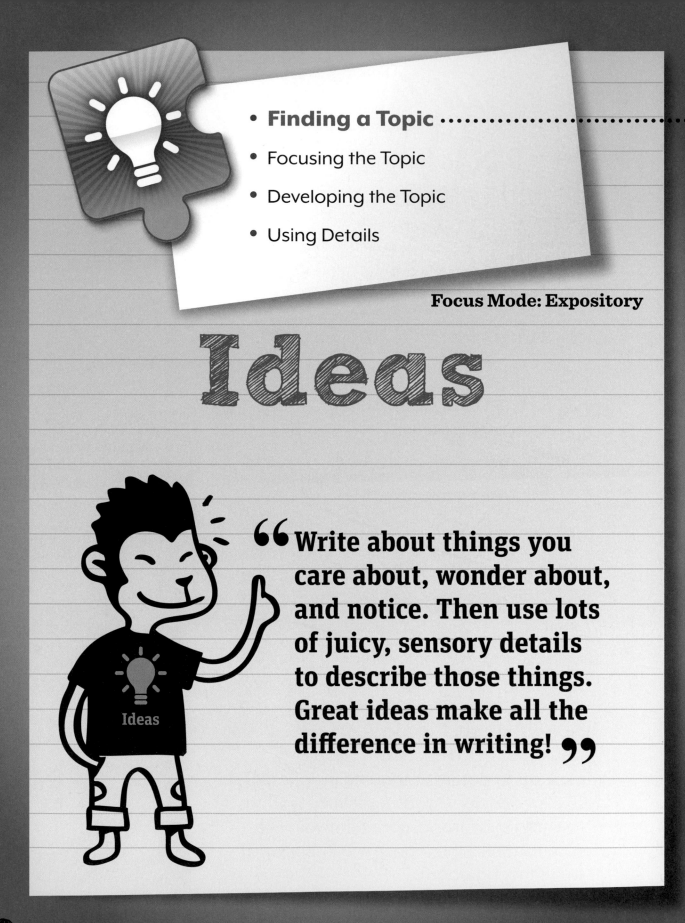

"Write about things you care about, wonder about, and notice. Then use lots of juicy, sensory details to describe those things. Great ideas make all the difference in writing!"

Finding a Topic

Topics are all around you—in things you experience every day. When you find the perfect topic, you know what to say. You see the "big picture." To find the perfect topic, think about what matters to you and let your ideas soar.

What's the connection between choosing beautiful flowers and choosing a good writing topic?

Ideas: **Finding a Topic**

Seed Ideas Sheet

Ideas for writing can pop into your head at any time or place. You need a place to jot them down so they don't get away. Start here. Fill in each section.

Things I notice

• Something interesting I saw

_____

_____

• Something unusual I heard

_____

_____

Things that worry me

• I think a lot about

_____

_____

• I get nervous when

_____

_____

Things that make me laugh

• Something funny I saw

_____

_____

• Something funny I did

_____

_____

Things I wonder about

• I'm curious about

_____

_____

• I want to know more about

_____

_____

Warm-Up 1

Whoa! Too many ideas. Pick one...and hit it out of the park.

How clear is the topic of this paragraph?

People all over the world play baseball. Little League games can be very exciting. Jackie Robinson was a great baseball player.

Revise the paragraph here or on a separate sheet.

Ideas

Think About

- Have I chosen a topic I really like?
- Do I have something new to say about this topic?
- Am I writing about what I know and care about?
- Have I gathered enough information so that I'm ready to write?

Ideas: Finding a Topic

Cynthia Rylant, author of *Snow*

Find a partner, discuss the questions below, and answer two of them.

1. Cynthia Rylant says that playing is great training for being a writer because it helps you "cook up interesting things in your head." What games do you like to play? How might these games help you become a better writer?

   _____

   _____

   _____

2. *Snow* is an entire picture book about one kind of weather. If you were going to write about weather, what kind of weather would you choose? Why?

   _____

   _____

   _____

3. Cynthia Rylant writes many types of books: picture books, short chapter books, nonfiction, novels for teens. She thinks picture books can be enjoyed by people of all ages. Do you agree? Why or why not?

   _____

   _____

   _____

Write-On Sheet

[Focus on Punctuation]

Write two sentences that show correct use of quotation marks.

1.

2.

66 The way to get good ideas is to get lots of ideas, and throw the bad ones away. 99

–Linus Pauling

[Snow Scenes]

Fill in the graphic organizer with information from *Snow* by Cynthia Rylant.

It's time for *snow* and tell!
Ideas

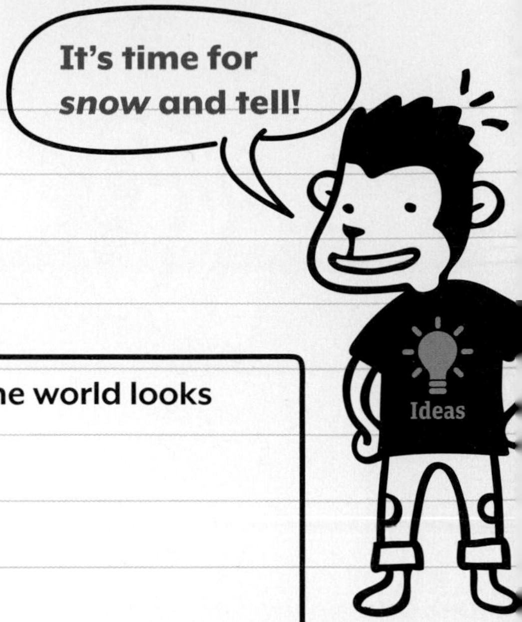

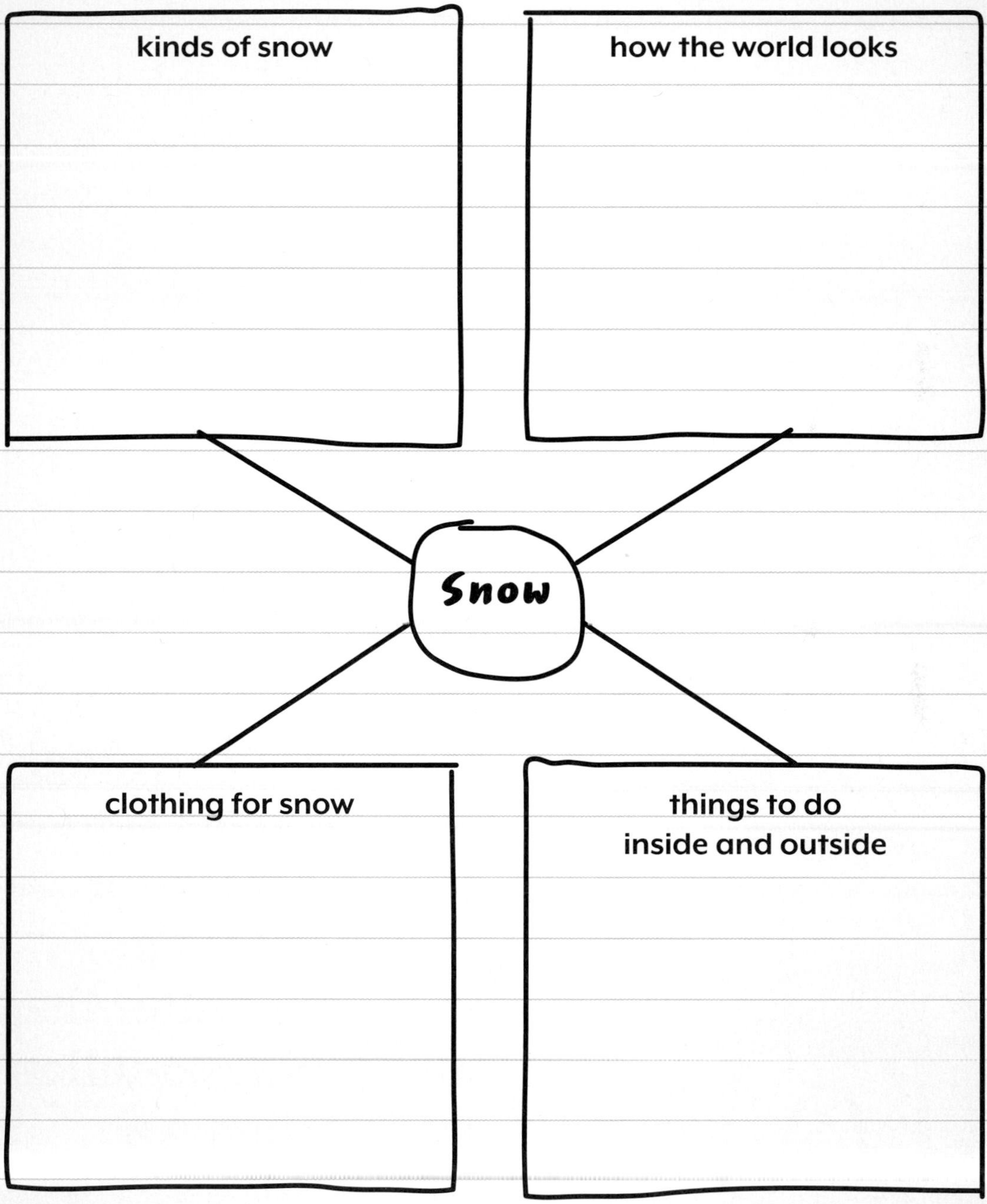

kinds of snow
how the world looks
Snow
clothing for snow
things to do inside and outside

- **Creating the Lead** ·····································
- Using Sequence Words and Transition Words
- Structuring the Body
- Ending With a Sense of Resolution

Focus Mode: Expository

Organization

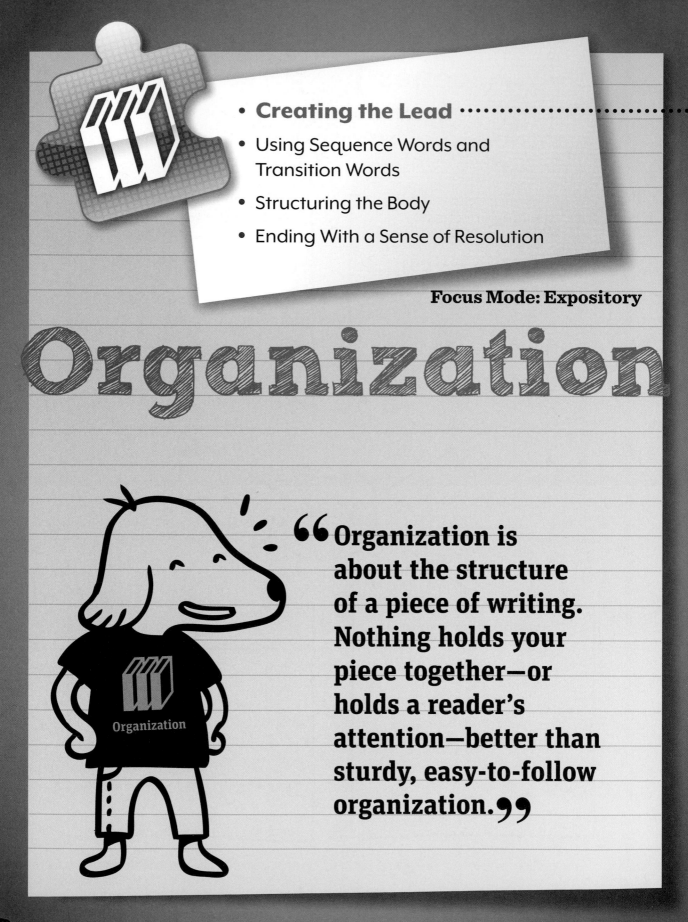

Organization

❝Organization is about the structure of a piece of writing. Nothing holds your piece together—or holds a reader's attention—better than sturdy, easy-to-follow organization.❞

Creating the Lead

The lead is the beginning of a piece of writing—
its first lines. A strong lead grabs the reader's
attention. It gives the reader something to think
about so that he or she wants to keep reading to
find out what you have to say.

How is a band conductor like the lead in a piece of writing?

Techniques for Creating the Lead

Use these techniques to create great leads. Your readers will sit up and take notice!

Lights, Camera, Action!

The writer makes something happen.

Example: I pressed my hand on the pup's backside in order to make him sit.

Single Word

The writer uses an important word as the first sentence, then follows it with more information.

Example: Sit. That is all I was trying to teach him. Simply, sit.

Fascinating Fact

The writer tells an interesting piece of information.

Example: The sit command is one of the easiest commands to teach a dog.

Compare It

The writer looks at the topic in different ways.

Example: Teaching a dog to sit is much easier than teaching a dog to roll over.

Listen Up

The writer describes a sound.

Example: "Yip! Yip!" That's the sound of a happy puppy.

I Wonder

The writer asks a question or a series of questions.

Example: Have you ever seen a dog do a cool trick and wondered how someone taught him or her to do it?

Warm-Up 2

WARNING: This lead could put fish to sleep!

How strong is this paragraph's lead?

Many people like to fish. It is easy. Put bait on the hook. When a fish bites, point the rod up and reel in the catch.

Revise the paragraph here or on a separate sheet.

Organization

Think About

• Did I give the reader something interesting to think about right from the start?

• Will the reader want to keep reading?

• Have I tried to get the reader's attention?

• Did I let the reader know what is coming?

Christine Taylor-Butler, author of
The Respiratory System

Read the information about Christine Taylor-Butler below and answer two of the questions.

Christine Taylor-Butler has always loved books, but she likes science, too. She worked as an engineer before switching careers. Why did she become an author? She wanted to write books that her daughters and their friends would love to read. So far, she has published more than 45 fiction and nonfiction books.

Engineers come up with scientific solutions to practical problems. Christine Taylor-Butler says her engineering background comes in handy when she researches a new book. She works hard to make sure her facts are correct. Of course, she works just as hard to find the right words to grab her readers' attention.

1. List two facts about Christine Taylor-Butler that you find interesting.

   _____

   _____

2. What might an author learn from kids that could help him or her find and develop ideas for books?

   _____

   _____

3. *The Respiratory System* is about sneezing, coughing, and breathing. It explains how the lungs work with other parts of the body. What would you like to know about this topic? Why?

   _____

   _____

Write-On Sheet

[My Spelling Words]

List your nine spelling words for the week here.

1.
2.
3.
4.
5.
6.
7.
8.
9.

> **"** What is the most boring way you could begin a research report . . . ? We all know. 'In this report I will tell you about . . .' **"**
>
> –Barry Lane

[Dive In!]

Write a new lead for Chapter 1 of Christine Taylor-Butler's *The Respiratory System.* Check the technique you will use and write an opening that is sure to leave readers breathless!

_____ Lights, Camera, Action!   _____ Compare It

_____ Single Word   _____ Listen Up

_____ Fascinating Fact   _____ I Wonder

_____

_____

_____

_____

_____

_____

_____

_____

_____

Go ahead. Leave them breathless. I know CPR!

- **Establishing a Tone** ....
- Conveying the Purpose
- Creating a Connection to the Audience
- Taking Risks to Create Voice

Focus Mode: Expository

Voice

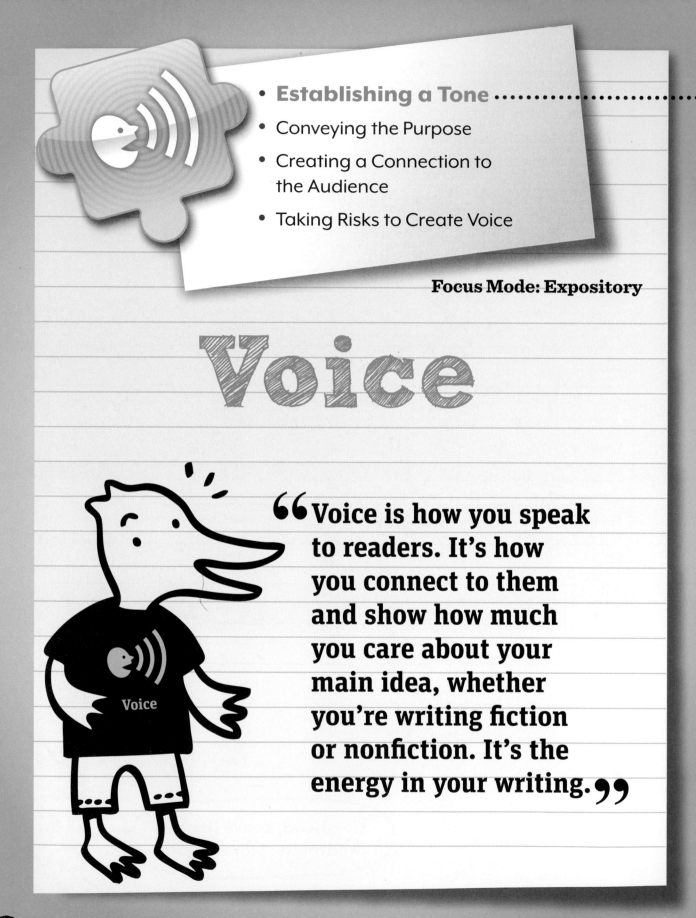

Voice

> Voice is how you speak to readers. It's how you connect to them and show how much you care about your main idea, whether you're writing fiction or nonfiction. It's the energy in your writing.

Establishing a Tone

When you talk, you express how you feel by your body language and the sound, or tone, of your voice. When you write, you express how you feel by the tone of the words you choose. The right tone lets readers know how you feel about the topic and how you want them to feel about it.

How are singing expressively and writing with a distinctive tone alike?

Name That Tone

What do you want your writing to express? Amazement? Anger? Pride? Excitement? Your tone tells the reader how you feel about the topic. Here are some examples.

happy	upset	believable	caring
convincing	scared	funny	excited
proud	angry	thrilled	serious
amazed	worried	curious	friendly

How do these writers feel about their topics? Read their paragraphs and write the tones you "hear."

1. Only twelve more hours until the first day of school, when I can finally see my best friends again. The summer was a real disappointment. Mark visited his grandparents, and my other friend Luis went to camp in another state! Mostly I took care of my little sister Olive. Boring. But tomorrow all that changes.

_____

2. *Hoo-oo-oo-oo!* How could that sound come from such a small owl? A full-grown screech owl stands only about eight inches tall. That's small for an owl. But that little bird makes a noise that sounds like a loud flute.

_____

3. *True or false? The air in a lightning bolt is about six times hotter than the surface of the sun.* True!! A lightning bolt is about 54,000 degrees Fahrenheit. Yes, that's six times hotter than the sun!

_____

4. It's 1884, a summer day in Louisville. Pete Brown swings the bat. Crack, he hits the ball! Pete's favorite bat breaks. John Hill, a woodworker, is watching the game. He makes Pete a new bat. The next day, Pete gets up to bat three times and has three hits.

_____

Warm-Up 3

Did you say laundry? Did anyone find a yellow sock?

How is the tone of this paragraph?

Doing the laundry takes several steps. Sort the clothes into three piles: light, dark, and color. Wash each one using laundry detergent. Wait until the washer finishes and move the clothes to the dryer. Fold the clothes when they are dry. Put the clothes away.

Revise the paragraph here or on a separate sheet.

Voice

Think About

- Can I name the primary voice of my writing (for example, happy, upset, wise, scared)?

- Have I changed the tone from the beginning to the end?

- Have I shown how I feel?

- Did I show that I care about this topic?

Preview

A Chef

In the spaces below, write what you think a chef does and what skills and talents you think he or she should have. What questions do you have about the job?

1. What I think a chef does:

   _____

   _____

   _____

   _____

2. Skills and talents a chef should have:

   _____

   _____

   _____

   _____

3. Questions I have about the job:

   _____

   _____

   _____

   _____

Write-On Sheet

Focus on Capitalization

Write two sentences that show correct use of capitalization.

1.

2.

> 66 Voice allows the reader to hear an individual human being speak from the page. 99
>
> –Donald M. Murray

[A Yummy Recipe]

Write a favorite recipe. Start by giving it a fun name. Use a tone in your writing that will make the reader want to go straight to the kitchen and try it out!

We're cooking now...

Name

Introduction

Ingredients

Equipment

Directions

1.

2.

3.

4.

5.

Talk about a tasty presentation!

[Expository Publishing Checklist]

Think you are ready to go public with your expository unit project? Use this form to make sure you've covered all the writing bases.

Check. Check. Quack. Check. Check.

I remembered to

☐ include facts and information that came from reliable sources.

☐ weave in details that show how much I know about my topic.

☐ develop the topic logically from beginning to end.

☐ use a voice that expresses my fascination for the topic.

☐ explain any unusual words, phrases, or concepts.

☐ read my piece aloud to check how it will sound to my reader.

☐ proofread my piece carefully and clean up problems with conventions.

The purpose of my piece is

_____

The part that works the best is

_____

What I hope readers will take away from my piece is

_____

Focus Mode: Narrative

Whether you're writing about aliens from outer space or an unforgettable vacation with your family, the main purpose of narrative writing is to tell a story. Your narrative pieces should include characters, a setting, events, and a problem to be solved—and maybe a surprise or two! They should capture your reader's interest and hang on to it, right to the end.

- **Applying Strong Verbs** ·······························
- Selecting Striking Words and Phrases
- Using Specific and Accurate Words
- Choosing Words That Deepen Meaning

Focus Mode: Narrative

Word Choice

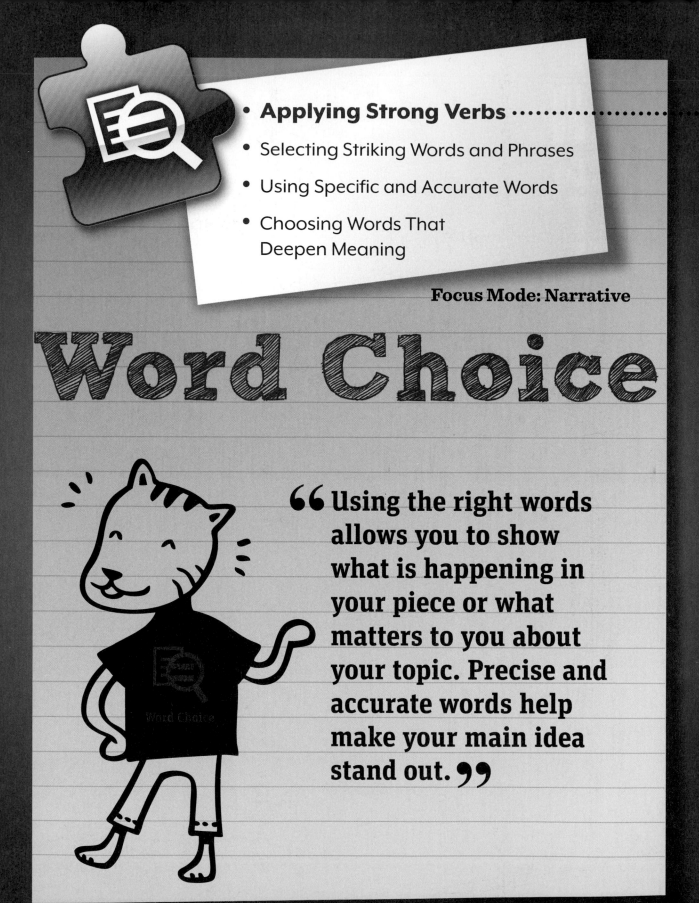

66 Using the right words allows you to show what is happening in your piece or what matters to you about your topic. Precise and accurate words help make your main idea stand out. 99

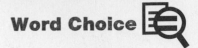

Applying Strong Verbs

You can hit a baseball or you can *whack* a baseball. You can read a comic book or *devour* it. Which would you rather do? Strong verbs pack a punch. They capture action precisely in one little word, putting your reader in the middle of the activity. With strong verbs, writing comes to life. It bursts with color and dazzles with light.

What do fireworks do that strong verbs also do?

Word Choice: **Applying Strong Verbs**

Make It Move!

The right verbs bring your writing to life. Keep a list of good ones. Start by imagining ways in which animals move. Be precise!

Animal	Verb
duck	waddles
cat	springs

Now liven up these sentences. Replace their boring verbs with more exciting, precise ones. Write each new sentence.

The tigers walked in the jungle.

_____

_____

Two horses ran in the field.

_____

_____

My little sister went out the door.

_____

_____

Warm-Up 4

How are the verbs in this paragraph?

I like to go to my grandma's house. Grandma and I have fun. We walk a lot. And we eat outside. She tells good stories.

Revise the paragraph here or on a separate sheet.

> You want verbs?
> I don't just walk. I prowl.
> I slink. I strut. Oh, yeah!

Think About

- Have I used action words?
- Did I stretch to get a better word–*scurry* rather than *run*?
- Do my verbs give my writing punch and pizzazz?
- Did I avoid *is, am, was, were, be, being,* and *been* whenever I could?

Word Choice: **Applying Strong Verbs**

Preview

A Cartoonist

In the spaces below, write down what you think a cartoonist does. Then list comic strips you like and questions you have about being a cartoonist.

1. What I think a cartoonist does:

_____

_____

_____

_____

2. Comic strips I especially like:

_____

_____

_____

_____

3. Questions I have about the job:

_____

_____

_____

_____

Write-On Sheet

[My Spelling Words]

List your nine spelling words for the week here.

1.
2.
3.
4.
5.
6.
7.
8.
9.

> " Nouns are the bones that give a sentence body. But verbs are the muscles that make it go. "
>
> –Mervin Block

[My Comic Strip]

It's time to create your own comic strip!
First, brainstorm some ideas.

My Ideas

Now choose the idea you like best.
Create a draft of your comic strip and give it a title.

Title _____

My Draft

When your comic strip looks the way you want it to,
draw your final version on a separate sheet.

How do you say "Those are nice verbs" in caveman?

Me caveman. Me like verbs.

Voice

- **Crafting Well-Built Sentences** ·············
- Varying Sentence Types
- Capturing Smooth and Rhythmic Flow
- Breaking the Rules to Create Fluency

Focus Mode: Narrative

Sentence Fluency

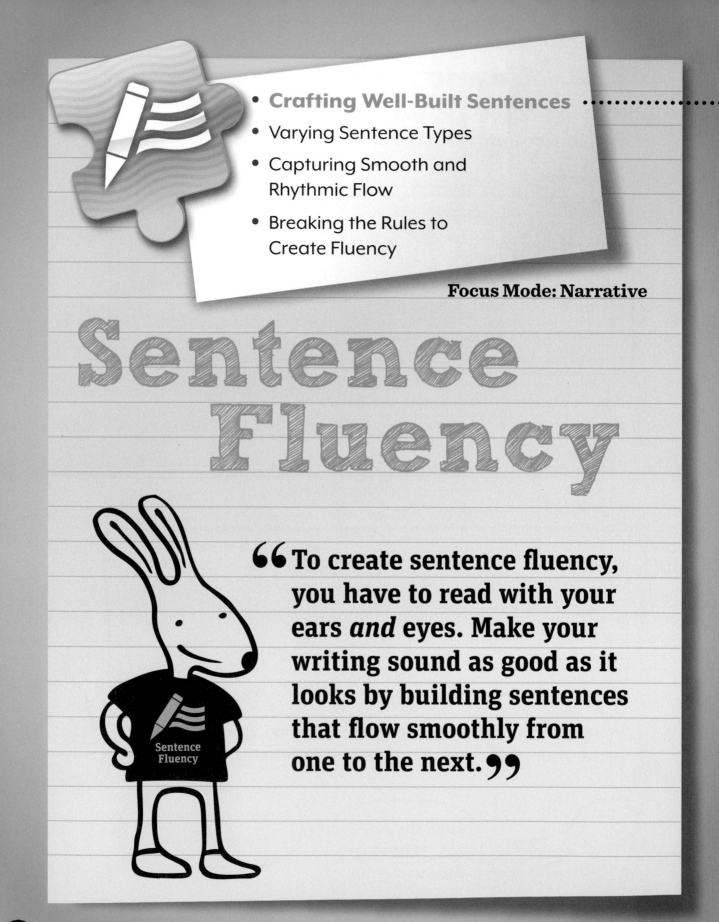

" To create sentence fluency, you have to read with your ears *and* eyes. Make your writing sound as good as it looks by building sentences that flow smoothly from one to the next. "

Crafting Well-Built Sentences

What does it mean for a piece of writing to have well-built sentences? It means the piece's sentences are not all short or all long. The sentences start with different words, not the same word over and over again. Words like *but, and,* and *so* join sentence parts. Well-built sentences move the reader through the piece.

How is crafting a well-built car like crafting a well-built sentence?

Build Them Up

Make the following sentences more interesting by expanding them one word at a time. Using words like *and, but,* or *or* will help.

An eagle can fly.

Add 1 word. _____

Add 1 word. _____

Add 1 word. _____

_____

Add 1 word. _____

_____

Add 1 word. _____

_____

I saw a tiger.

Add 1 word. _____

Add 1 word. _____

Add 1 word. _____

_____

Add 1 word. _____

_____

Add 1 word. _____

_____

Warm-Up 5

These sentences need some rhythm and flow. (And maybe a little floss!)

Are the sentences in this paragraph well built?

I lost two more teeth. I lost my two pointy front teeth. They were wiggly for a long time. They came out on the same day.

Revise the paragraph here or on a separate sheet.

Think About

- Do my sentences begin in different ways?
- Are my sentences of different lengths?
- Are my sentences grammatically correct unless I broke rules for impact?
- Have I used conjunctions such as *but, and,* and *so* to connect parts of sentences?

Rose Blue and Corinne J. Naden

Ron's Big Mission

Read the information about Rose Blue and Corinne Naden below and answer two of the questions.

Rose Blue wrote fiction, song lyrics, and TV screenplays before she started writing nonfiction. Then she met another nonfiction writer, Corinne Naden, who had worked as an editor and news writer. The two began writing together. As a team, they wrote more than 40 biographies, including a long book about astronaut Ron McNair.

Sometimes, authors start out writing one book, and end up having enough material for two books. That's what happened to this author team. An event from McNair's childhood deserved to be told in a picture book, in their opinion. That book is *Ron's Big Mission*.

1. If you were writing a biography, would you want to work on your own or with a writing partner? Why?

   _____

   _____

2. How might experience writing song lyrics, plays, and news articles help picture book writers craft sentences?

   _____

   _____

3. Think of someone famous. What would you like to know about his or her childhood? How could you find out?

   _____

   _____

Write-On Sheet

[Focus on Grammar and Usage]

Write two sentences that contain correct irregular plural nouns.

1.

2.

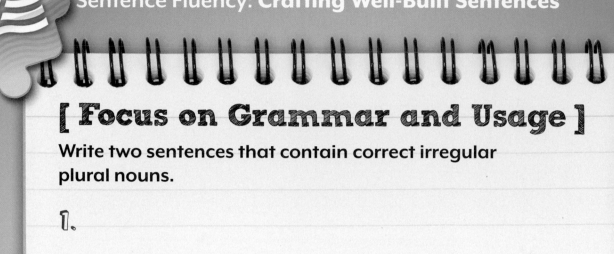

66 No one should ever have to read a sentence twice because of the way it is put together. 99

–Wilson Follett

[Super Sentences]

This paragraph needs a makeover. Hop to it!

Read aloud the paragraph in the box. It doesn't sound quite right, does it? Rewrite it using two techniques for creating sentence fluency.

> Ron took a deep breath. He lifted his head high. He went inside.

• **Begin the sentences in different ways.**

_____

_____

_____

_____

_____

• **Make the sentences different lengths. Add words, cut words, and combine sentences by using conjunctions (*but, and, so*).**

_____

_____

_____

_____

- Finding a Topic
- **Focusing the Topic** ··············
- Developing the Topic
- Using Details

Focus Mode: Narrative

Ideas

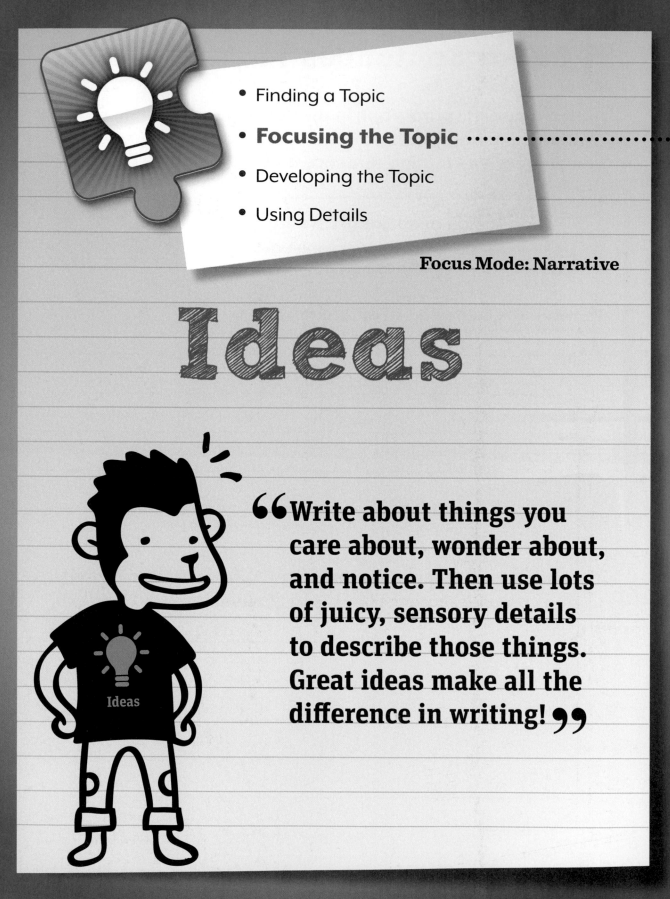

"Write about things you care about, wonder about, and notice. Then use lots of juicy, sensory details to describe those things. Great ideas make all the difference in writing! "

Focusing the Topic

When you focus your topic, you zero in on something important or interesting about it. You make your writing clear and strong because you're not taking on the whole world—you're taking on one really cool corner of it.

How are using binoculars and focusing a topic similar?

Narrow It!

Narrow your big topic until you have a focused one.

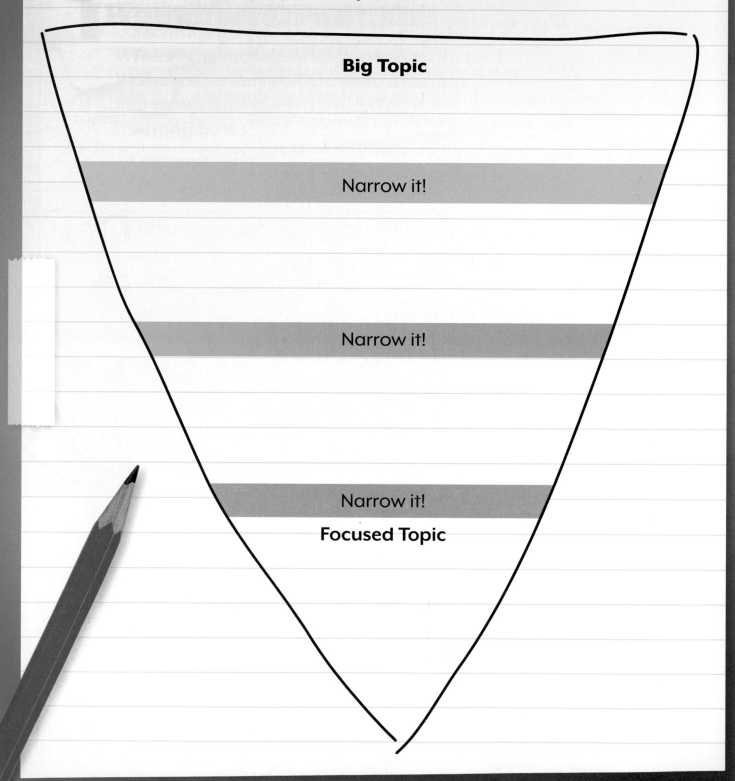

Big Topic

Narrow it!

Narrow it!

Narrow it!

Focused Topic

Warm-Up 6

Am I losing my mind, or is this paragraph out of focus?

Is the topic of this paragraph focused?

I was really nervous about starting a new school in a new city. But this year is great so far. I've made lots of new friends. And my class went on some field trips.

Revise the paragraph here or on a separate sheet.

Think About

- Have I zeroed in on one small part of a bigger idea?
- Can I sum up my idea in a simple sentence?
- Have I chosen the information that captures my idea best?
- Have I thought deeply about what the reader will need to know?

Ideas: **Focusing the Topic**

Ed Young, author of *Lon Po Po*

Read the information about Ed Young and answer two of the questions below.

Ed Young grew up in China. He loved listening to his father tell stories. He also loved drawing on every scrap of paper he found. When he grew up, he came to the United States to study architecture, but decided to become an illustrator. He didn't think he could write books until his editor suggested he record himself telling a story. That story was a Chinese folktale about a hungry wolf, which Young had heard as a boy. It became *Lon Po Po*, the first of more than 30 award-winning books he has written and illustrated.

"There are things that words do that pictures never can," says Young. "And there are images that words never can describe."

1. How do you think childhood experiences helped Ed Young find and focus the topic for *Lon Po Po*?

   _____

   _____

   _____

2. What did Ed Young do to find the confidence to write *Lon Po Po*? What other things could he have done to get himself ready to write?

   _____

   _____

3. Do you agree that "there are things that words do that pictures never can"? Explain why or why not.

   _____

   _____

Write-On Sheet

[My Spelling Words]

List your nine spelling words for the week here.

1.
2.
3.
4.
5.
6.
7.
8.
9.

> " Ideas are the cheapest part of the writing. They are free. The hard part is what you do with ideas you've gathered. "
>
> –Jane Yolen

[That Big Bad Wolf!]

Wolf stories are HOWL-arious!

Check off only the sentences that are important to each story. Then write each story's focus.

Little Red Riding Hood

_____ She liked walking in the woods.

_____ She was helpful to her grandmother.

_____ The wolf pretended to be her grandmother.

_____ The wolf lived in the woods.

_____ A woodcutter rescued her.

_____ The wolf tricked her and ate her.

Lon Po Po

_____ A mother went to visit Grandmother on her birthday.

_____ Lon Po Po did not fool the girls.

_____ The tree was very tall.

_____ The girls tricked Lon Po Po.

_____ Gingko nuts are very tasty.

_____ Lon Po Po wanted to eat the girls.

Focus of Little Red Riding Hood

Focus of Lon Po Po

[Narrative Publishing Checklist]

Think you are ready to go public with your narrative unit project? Use this form to make sure you've covered all the writing bases.

Don't gallop through this page, cowboy!

I remembered to

- [ ] develop a fascinating story line with interesting characters.
- [ ] include a time and a place that work well with the story line.
- [ ] present a problem and solution.
- [ ] tell the story chronologically.
- [ ] use an active voice to entertain, surprise, and challenge the reader.
- [ ] choose words that enhance the characters, time, and place.
- [ ] read my piece aloud to check for how it will sound to my reader.
- [ ] proofread my piece carefully and clean up problems with conventions.

The purpose of my piece is

_____

My favorite part is where

_____

What I hope readers will find most memorable about my piece is

_____

Focus Mode: Persuasive

Whether you're asking your parents to
let you take karate or convincing your
friend to come over and watch a movie,
the main purpose of persuasive writing
is to construct an argument. Your piece
should state a position clearly and stick
with that position. You need to offer
good, sound reasoning. And use a
strong, confident voice to let your reader
know you mean business.

- Creating the Lead
- **Using Sequence Words and Transition Words** ....
- Structuring the Body
- Ending With a Sense of Resolution

Focus Mode: Persuasive

Organization

66 **Organization is about the structure of a piece of writing. Nothing holds your piece together—or holds a reader's attention—better than sturdy, easy-to-follow organization.** 99

Using Sequence Words and Transition Words

Road signs help us move from Point A to Point B. Sequence words (such as *next* and *finally*) in a piece of writing do something similar. They tell you when something important is coming up. Transition words (such as *but* and *also*) are the signs that tell you to change direction or pay attention to something different.

How are sequence words and transition words like the signs on a highway?

What's the Order?

The order of these sentences is wacky. Number them from 1 to 6 to straighten them out.

_____ Just then, my neighbor drove by and gave me a lift.

_____ All my troubles started at 3:00.

_____ Next, I missed the school bus.

_____ First, it started to rain when I left school, and I got soaked.

_____ Finally, I got home, only to be scolded because I was late for my piano lesson.

_____ After that, I started to walk home.

Now number these sentences from 1 to 5 to put them in a more logical order. Circle the words that helped you figure out the order.

_____ Finally, it's good for kids to make some choices for themselves.

_____ For instance, I think kids should be able to decide when to go to bed.

_____ Also, you can't tell someone "Sleep!" and they do it.

_____ I don't think parents should have so many rules for their kids.

_____ First of all, kids know when they're sleepy. No one has to tell them.

Warm-Up 7

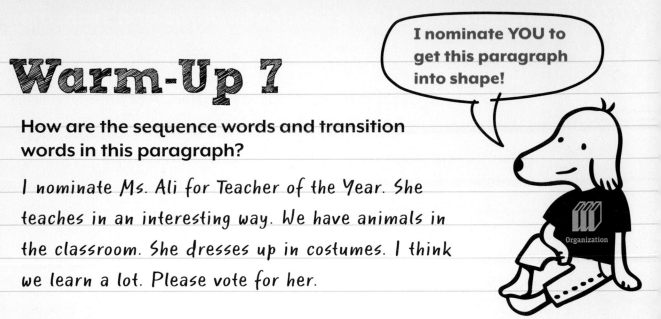

I nominate YOU to get this paragraph into shape!

How are the sequence words and transition words in this paragraph?

I nominate Ms. Ali for Teacher of the Year. She teaches in an interesting way. We have animals in the classroom. She dresses up in costumes. I think we learn a lot. Please vote for her.

Revise the paragraph here or on a separate sheet.

Think About

- Have I used sequence words such as *later, then,* and *meanwhile*?
- Did I use a variety of transition words such as *however, because, also,* and *for instance*?
- Have I shown how the ideas connect from sentence to sentence?
- Does my organization make sense from paragraph to paragraph?

Preview

Mark Teague, author of *LaRue Across America: Postcards From the Vacation*

Directions: Find a partner, discuss the questions below, and answer two of them.

1. When he wrote his first book, Mark Teague was working in a bookstore. How might working in a bookstore help someone decide to become a writer?

_____

_____

_____

2. Mark Teague has written and illustrated four books about a dog named Ike LaRue. Teague is also the author of *The Secret Shortcut, Pigsty, Funny Farm, How I Spent My Summer Vacation*, and *Firehouse!* Have you read any of these books? Which one would you most like to read? Why?

_____

_____

_____

3. Filling notebooks with drawings helps Mark Teague plan his books. What kinds of things would you put in your own writer's notebook?

_____

_____

_____

Write-On Sheet

[Focus on Punctuation]

Write two sentences that contain correct use of abbreviations.

1. _____

   _____

2. _____

   _____

"Only connect! **"**

–E. M. Forster

[Find the Links]

Mark Teague uses sequence words and transition words to connect details in *LaRue Across America*. Write down the ones he uses in Ike's postcards.

If you ask me, a vacation with cats is NO vacation at all!

Sequence Words	Transition Words

Write a postcard from the cats to Mrs. Hibbins telling her about the vacation. Use sequence words and transition words to link details.

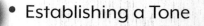

- Establishing a Tone
- **Conveying the Purpose** ·····························
- Creating a Connection to the Audience
- Taking Risks to Create Voice

Focus Mode: Persuasive

Voice

> **Voice is how you speak to readers. It's how you connect to them and show how much you care about your main idea, whether you're writing fiction or nonfiction. It's the energy in your writing.**

Voice

Conveying the Purpose

In a piece of writing, the voice you use should match your purpose for writing the piece. If you're writing a letter of thanks, your tone might be grateful. But if you're writing a letter of complaint, your tone might be frustrated. Use your voice to convey what you think and how you feel. Don't leave any doubt in your reader's mind.

How is writing a paper like making a speech?

What's Its Purpose?

Read the passages in the boxes. Then choose a purpose and tone of voice for each one.

Purposes

to inform   to persuade   to tell a story

Tones

worried   determined   surprised

happy   anxious   nervous

friendly   excited

knowledgeable

Ribbit, ribbit. Have you ever heard a frog sing? It's such an interesting sound. Frogs sing to attract mates, mark their territory, or alert other frogs to changing weather. In some countries, such as Japan, frogs are symbols of good luck.

➡ Purpose _____

➡ Tone _____

Frogs may be small, but their importance is big! When a frog is endangered, it affects many other animals—including us. Frogs eat insects. Fewer frogs mean more bugs to damage crops, carry diseases, and bug us. More than 120 species of frogs have become extinct. You can help save the ones that are left. Find out how TODAY.

➡ Purpose _____

➡ Tone _____

The hubbub in the school cafeteria suddenly got three times louder. What looked like a green blob was leaping across the room. Jessie's pet frog was jumping around like a ping-pong ball. With a mighty bound, it landed right on the sandwich of the new boy in Jessie's class, Hiroki.
"I'm really sorry," mumbled Jessie.
"No problem," said Hiroki, smiling. "Where I come from, frogs are good luck. What a great welcome!"

➡ Purpose _____

➡ Tone _____

Warm-Up 8

Writing is like riding a bike. You write. You fall down. You get back up and write again!

Is the writer's purpose for writing this paragraph clear?

I see many people riding bikes these days. Some people go to work or school on bikes to cut down on pollution. That's a good idea. They should follow rules of the road. I saw a scary thing happen last week.

Revise the paragraph here or on a separate sheet.

Think About

- Is the purpose of my writing clear?
- Does my point of view come through?
- Is this the right tone for this kind of writing?
- Have I used strong voice throughout this piece?

Preview

A Publicist

Work with a partner. Write about what you think a publicist does. What questions do you have about the job?

1. What kind of writing I think a publicist does and where I've seen it:

_____

_____

_____

_____

2. A publicist lets people know about things that are going on. How do you think a publicist gets started on a piece of writing?

_____

_____

_____

_____

3. Questions I have about the job of a publicist:

_____

_____

_____

_____

Write-On Sheet

[My Spelling Words]

List your nine spelling words for the week here.

1.
2.
3.
4.
5.
6.
7.
8.
9.

" Don't write merely to be understood. Write so that you cannot possibly be misunderstood. "

–Robert Louis Stevenson

[Best Birthday Ever]

Let's not play Pin the Tail on the Duck! Okay?!

Read the activities in the chart below. Then add more activities that you and your friends would like to do.

Party Activities

At a Science and Space Museum	At an Art Museum	At a History Museum
Use toothpicks and marshmallows to make structures that stand strong. Make spinning helicopters from paper and then crank them up to the ceiling to see if they fly ... or fall.	Use food coloring and shaving cream to make a beautiful piece of marbled art. Go on a team scavenger hunt. Search for answers to tricky questions about mummies, knights, and palace rooms.	Find out what creatures roamed the state millions of years ago. Grab your tools to unearth fossils. Travel back to colonial America. Dress in period clothing and play Roll the Hoop or Bob for Apples.

Imagine you are the publicist for one of the museums. On a separate **sheet**, write a paragraph to persuade kids that a birthday party at your museum would be the best party ever.

- Applying Strong Verbs
- **Selecting Striking Words and Phrases** ·················
- Using Specific and Accurate Words
- Choosing Words That Deepen Meaning

Focus Mode: Persuasive

Word Choice

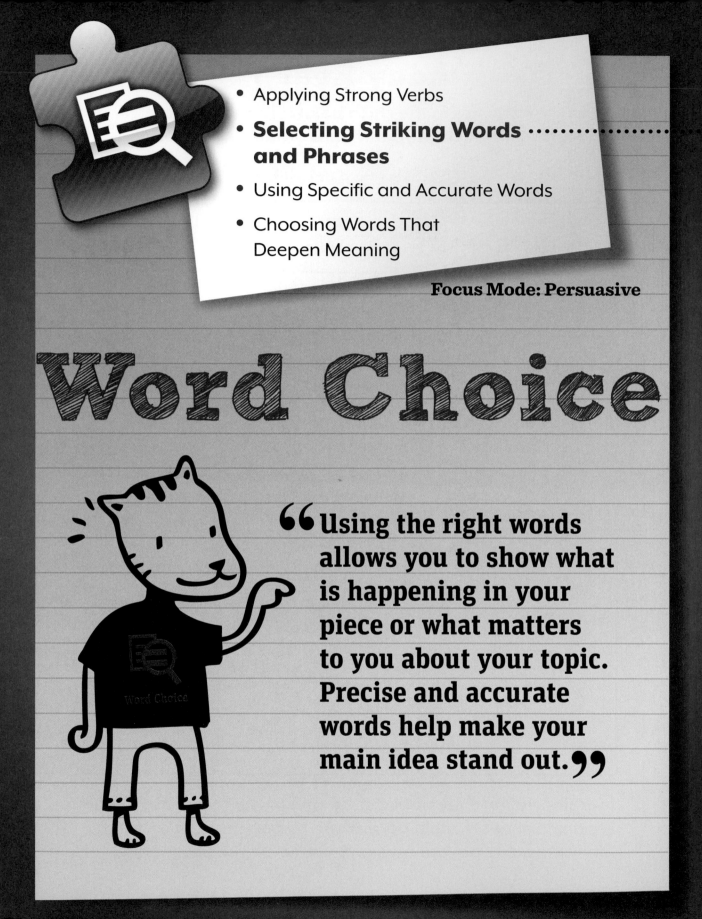

❝Using the right words allows you to show what is happening in your piece or what matters to you about your topic. Precise and accurate words help make your main idea stand out.❞

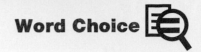

Selecting Striking Words and Phrases

Striking words and phrases make your writing sparkle. They help readers feel as if they're inside your piece, rather than on the sidelines. Precise, descriptive words and phrases linger in the mind. Readers will think about the piece long after they have finished reading it. Think bling, not blah!

How are striking words and phrases like these fancy costumes?

Word Choice: **Selecting Striking Words and Phrases**

Sparkling Sentences

Here are three good ways to create striking words and phrases. Match each way to the example. Write the number in the blank.

You Can Use

1. Synonyms: Use interesting words to replace ordinary ones.

terrified	instead of scared
brilliant	instead of smart
swift	instead of fast

2. Alliteration: Use words that begin with the same sound.

√ the **b**ouncing **b**us

√ an **a**larming **a**ngry **a**lligator

√ the **s**pinning **s**pider

3. Similes: Use comparisons with the words *as* or *like*.

√ a tree **as** tall as a five-story building

√ a voice **like** thunder

Examples

_____ These stale raisins are like pebbles.

_____ Watch out for the buzzing bumblebees!

_____ "Your new dress is gorgeous!" cried Katie.

_____ The child could barely lift his bulging backpack.

_____ Putting a new bike together is challenging.

_____ Her nose felt as cold as a popsicle.

_____ The air was filled with the aroma of pizza.

_____ Melted, mushy marshmallows are a favorite treat.

Try This! Use striking words and phrases to make this sentence sparkle:

We saw a lot of pretty butterflies.

Warm-Up 9

Dude! This writing needs a little spice ....

How striking are the words and phrases in this paragraph?

The food at school isn't very good. Actually, it's pretty bad. It does not have much taste, and it's boring to eat the same thing every day. Will you sign my petition? I'm asking the principal to get better food.

Revise the paragraph here or on a separate sheet.

Think About

- Did I try to use words that sound "just right"?
- Did I try hyphenating several shorter words to make an interesting-sounding new word?
- Did I try putting words with the same sound together?
- Did I read my piece aloud to find at least one or two moments I love?

Preview

Lisa Yee, author of *Bobby the Brave (Sometimes)*

Read the information about Lisa Yee below and answer two of the questions.

"Work hard. Be creative. Have fun." That's the motto of Magic Pencil, a company Lisa Yee runs with her husband. Lisa Yee has worked as an inventor and a hand model, and for Walt Disney World, where she once got to dress as Mickey Mouse. She has done all kinds of writing: TV ads, scripts, speeches—and books.

Lisa Yee gets ideas for stories by observing what's going on around her. She gets to know her characters as she writes about them. Each of them is special to her for a different reason. For example, the main character in *Bobby the Brave* is a "perfectly normal fourth grader who gets into perfectly crazy situations."

1. List two facts about Lisa Yee that you find interesting.

_____

_____

2. Ads must grab readers' attention in just a few words. How do you think creating ads might help a writer become skilled at selecting striking words and phrases?

_____

_____

3. Think about Magic Pencil's motto: "Work hard. Be creative. Have fun." How might living by these words help you as a writer?

_____

_____

Write-On Sheet

Word Choice: Selecting Striking Words and Phrases

[Focus on Grammar and Usage]

Write two sentences that contain correct use of singular and plural nouns.

1. _____

   _____

   _____

2. _____

   _____

   _____

66 All my life I've looked at words as though I were seeing them for the first time. 99

–Ernest Hemingway

[Lisa Yee's Striking Words and Phrases]

Go for the BOLD!

For *Bobby the Brave*, Lisa Yee could have written the words and phrases in column 1. But she didn't! Fill in the striking words and phrases that she wrote instead.

Ordinary Words and Phrases	Lisa Yee's Striking Words and Phrases
This is an interesting topic.	
A few students were very nervous.	
There was a list of fears on the board.	
Bring food like pizza.	

[Persuasive Publishing Checklist]

Think you are ready to go public with your persuasive unit project? Use this form to make sure you've covered all the writing bases.

Get ready! It's show time!

Presentation

I remembered to

- ☐ state my position on the topic clearly and stick with it.
- ☐ offer good, sound reasoning that the reader can relate to.
- ☐ provide solid facts, opinions, and examples that are based on reliable, objective sources.
- ☐ expose weaknesses in other positions.
- ☐ develop my argument using solid reasoning from beginning to end.
- ☐ use a compelling, confident voice to add credibility.
- ☐ explain any unusual words, phrases, or concepts.
- ☐ read my piece aloud to check how it will sound to my reader.
- ☐ proofread my piece carefully and clean up conventions.

The purpose of my piece is

_____

The most critical point I make is

_____

What I hope readers will take away from my piece is

_____

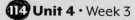

Focus Mode: Expository

Whether your topic is brown bears, bagels, or Botswana, the main purpose of expository writing is to inform or explain. That said, your piece does not need to be a list of facts. In reality, it shouldn't be. Think about including fascinating details, intriguing insights, and life experiences. Good expository writing is written in a strong, confident voice—a voice that tells the reader you know what you're talking about.

- Crafting Well-Built Sentences
- **Varying Sentence Types** ....
- Capturing Smooth and Rhythmic Flow
- Breaking the "Rules" to Create Fluency

Focus Mode: Expository

Sentence Fluency

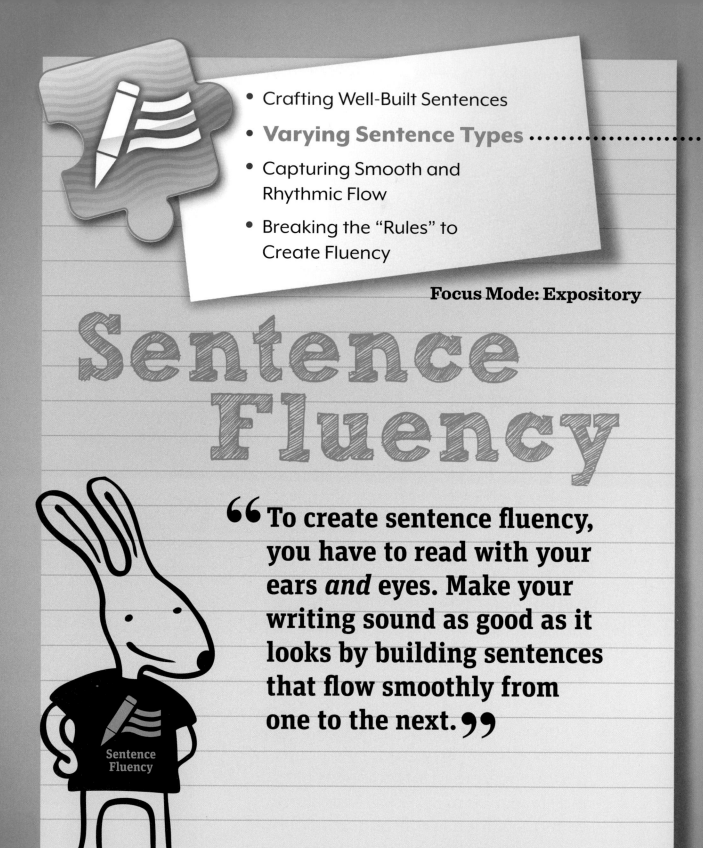

❝To create sentence fluency, you have to read with your ears *and* eyes. Make your writing sound as good as it looks by building sentences that flow smoothly from one to the next.❞

Sentence Fluency

Varying Sentence Types

Do you want the secret to making your writing sound great? Include sentences of all kinds—short ones, long ones, and medium-size ones. Include statements, questions, commands, and exclamations. When you mix up your sentences, you bring color and variety to your writing.

A great farmers market offers all kinds of fruits and vegetables. A great piece of writing offers all kinds of sentences. What else offers all kinds of things?

Readers Theater

Check out the four kinds of sentences. Then read the script with two classmates while audience members name each sentence.

Statement	Command
Bananas are my favorite food.	Throw away that banana peel.
Question	**Exclamation**
Is this banana ripe?	Banana smoothies are yummy!

Reader 1:   I got milk, yogurt, bananas, and strawberries to make smoothies.

Reader 2:   How do we make them?

Reader 1:   You measure one cup milk, one cup yogurt, and one-fourth cup of strawberries.

Reader 2:   Then what do we do?

Reader 3:   Put everything in a blender with one sliced banana.

Reader 1:   Now push the "blend" button.

Reader 2:   Yikes, the lid was not on the blender!

Reader 3:   Yuck, we're wearing banana smoothie!

Reader 1:   What should we do?

Reader 3:   Get a sponge and clean up the mess.

Reader 2:   Let's try again.

Reader 3:   This time we'll follow the recipe and put the lid on the blender.

ALL: Okay, everyone, here we go!

Warm-Up 10

Improving this paragraph will be a breeze!

How is this paragraph's sentence variety?

Windy days are fun. There are so many things to do. You can fly a kite. You can jump in a leaf pile. You can run with the wind at your back. You can read. You can listen to the wind on the roof.

Revise the paragraph here or on a separate sheet.

Think About

- Did I include different kinds of sentences?
- Are some of my sentences longer than others?
- Are some of my sentences simple?
- Did I intermingle sentence types?

Preview

Joanne Ryder, author of *Panda Kindergarten*

Work with a partner to answer three of the questions below.

1. Joanne Ryder wrote *Panda Kindergarten, A Pair of Polar Bears,* and *Little Panda.* What do these books have in common?

_____

_____

2. In her books, Joanne Ryder often asks kids to imagine what it's like being different animals. What animal would you choose to be? Why?

_____

_____

3. The author says that she sometimes gets an idea for a nonfiction book from an amazing animal fact she read. Where do you get ideas for your nonfiction pieces?

_____

_____

4. Joanne Ryder is filled with curiosity. How does being curious help a writer?

_____

_____

5. What animal would you like Joanna Ryder to write about next? Why?

_____

_____

Write-On Sheet

[My Spelling Words]

List your nine spelling words for the week here.

1.
2.
3.
4.
5.
6.
7.
8.
9.

"Always write (and read) with the ear, not the eye. You should hear every sentence you write as if it was being read aloud or spoken."

—C. S. Lewis

[Listen! Which Kind?]

What kinds of sentences does *Panda Kindergarten* contain? For every sentence you hear, check a box.

Statement   ☐ ☐ ☐ ☐

Question   ☐ ☐ ☐ ☐

Command   ☐ ☐ ☐ ☐

Exclamation   ☐ ☐ ☐ ☐

> I have very *hoppy* memories of bunny kindergarten.

What are some things you learned from *Panda Kindergarten*? Write a paragraph. Be sure to include all kinds of sentences.

- Finding a Topic
- Focusing the Topic
- **Developing the Topic** ·······················
- Using Details

Focus Mode: Expository

Ideas

❝Write about things you care about, wonder about, and notice. Then use lots of juicy, sensory details to describe those things. Great ideas make all the difference in writing!❞

Developing the Topic

When you develop your topic, you flesh out your main idea. You think deeply about why you're writing the piece and what your reader needs to know to understand it. You stretch to express yourself. Your topic blossoms.

With water and sunlight, a flower blossoms. What does a writing topic need to blossom?

Talk About a Topic

Prepare a talk on a topic of your choice.

My Topic _____

My Notes _____

_____

_____

_____

_____

_____

Questions I Have About My Classmates' Talks

A question for _____ :

_____

A question for _____ :

_____

A question for _____ :

_____

A question for _____ :

_____

Warm-Up 11

Monkey around with this paragraph. Check your facts, and make it more *egg*-citing!

Is this paragraph's topic developed?

Emperor penguins live in a cold place up north. The mother emperor penguin lays an egg and leaves. The father penguin takes care of the egg. When the egg hatches, the mother comes back and the father takes his time leaving so he can eat.

Revise the paragraph here or on a separate sheet.

Think About

- Am I sure my information is right?
- Are my details chock-full of interesting information?
- Have I used details that show new thinking about this idea?
- Will my reader believe what I say about this topic?

Ideas: **Developing the Topic**

Preview

Quiara Alegría Hudes, author of
Welcome to My Neighborhood!
Work with a partner to answer two of the questions below.

1. The author got her idea for *Welcome to My Neighborhood!* from her own neighborhood. Why do you think she chose that topic? How do you think her personal experience helped her develop the topic fully?

   _____

   _____

2. Quiara Alegría Hudes is also a musician—and she writes plays. How do you think being a musician might help her as a writer? (Hint: What about sentence fluency?)

   _____

   _____

3. Quiara Alegría Hudes wrote plays as a child. Her first play was produced when she was in tenth grade. What's a skill or interest that you have now? Do you think you might still have that interest when you grow up?

   _____

   _____

4. Alegría likes to write both plays and children's books. How do you think a play might be different from a book?

   _____

   _____

Write-On Sheet

[Focus on Grammar and Usage]

Write two sentences that contain forms of the verb *to be*.
Write one sentence in the present tense and the other
in the past tense.

1. _____

   _____

2. _____

   _____

66 The task of a writer consists in being able to make something out of an idea. 99

—Thomas Mann

[Stop, Look, and Listen!]

What's special about Quiara Alegría Hudes's neighborhood?
Write some of the information you learned about it.

Places

People

Things

Welcome to My Neighborhood!

Sounds

Tastes

A banana store would be very a-*peel*-ing!

- Creating the Lead
- Using Sequence Words and Transition Words
- **Structuring the Body** ....
- Ending With a Sense of Resolution

Focus Mode: Expository

Organization

Organization

66 **Organization is about the structure of a piece of writing. Nothing holds your piece together—or holds a reader's attention—better than sturdy, easy-to-follow organization.** 99

Structuring the Body

When you apply this key quality well, you create a piece that is a breeze to read. You present details logically and use them to support your big idea. You slow down and speed up at just the right points. Your piece is well formed and solid.

How is building a sand castle like structuring the body of a piece of writing?

Let's Get Organized!

Draw a symbol to stand for each type of text structure.

Sequence or Time Order

Explains a series of events or steps in a process

Examples:

- getting ready for school
- how crayons are made
- a day in the life of a veterinarian

Description or List

Provides information about a person, place, or thing

Examples:

- the funniest kid I know
- baseball parks I want to visit
- favorite songs

Problem and Solution

Presents a tough situation and explains how to fix it

Examples:

- a flat bike tire
- a tornado warning
- first day at a new school

Warm-Up 12

Where does this paragraph begin and end? Reading it reminds me of chasing my own tail!

How is the structure of this paragraph?

Add the cut-up fruit to the bowl. Wash the containers. It's the best snack ever. Pick your favorite fruit. Add yogurt. Stir hard. Add crushed ice. Pour into a glass. Tired of the same after-school snack?

Revise the paragraph here or on a separate sheet.

Think About

- Have I shown the reader where to slow down and where to speed up?
- Do all the details fit where they are placed?
- Will the reader find it easy to follow my ideas?
- Does the organization help the main idea stand out?

Preview

A Product Developer

In the spaces below, fill in your thoughts about what a product developer does.

1. What I think a product developer does:

   _____

   _____

   _____

   _____

2. How might a product developer's writing change, depending on the product?

   _____

   _____

   _____

   _____

3. What I imagine to be the toughest part of the product developer's job:

   _____

   _____

   _____

   _____

Write-On Sheet

[My Spelling Words]

List your nine spelling words for the week here.

1.
2.
3.
4.
5.
6.
7.
8.
9.

> " Organizing is what you do before you do something, so that when you do it, it's not all mixed-up. "
>
> –A. A. Milne

[New Buddy]

Create a new buddy. Write a product description in a voice that fits him or her. Then draw a picture of your buddy.

Name:

Nickname:

Eye Color:

Hair Color:

Motto:

This is my story.

_____

_____

_____

_____

_____

_____

_____

_____

[Expository Publishing Checklist]

Think you are ready to go public with your expository unit project? Use this form to make sure you've covered all the writing bases.

I remembered to

☐ include facts and information that came from reliable sources.

☐ weave in details that show how much I know about my topic.

☐ develop the topic logically from beginning to end.

☐ use a voice that expresses my fascination for the topic.

☐ explain any unusual words, phrases, or concepts.

☐ read my piece aloud to check how it will sound to my reader.

☐ proofread my piece carefully and clean up problems with conventions.

Meowzah! Get ready for Expository Glory!

The purpose of my piece is

_____

The part that works best is

_____

What I hope readers will take away from my piece is

_____

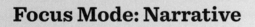

Focus Mode: Narrative

Whether you're writing about your best birthday ever or an imaginary beast that lives under your bed, the main purpose of narrative writing is to tell a story. Your narrative pieces should include characters, a setting, events, and a problem to be solved . . . and maybe a surprise or two. Your story should capture your reader's interest and hang on to it!

- Establishing a Tone
- Conveying the Purpose
- **Creating a Connection to the Audience** ....
- Taking Risks to Create Voice

Focus Mode: Narrative

Voice

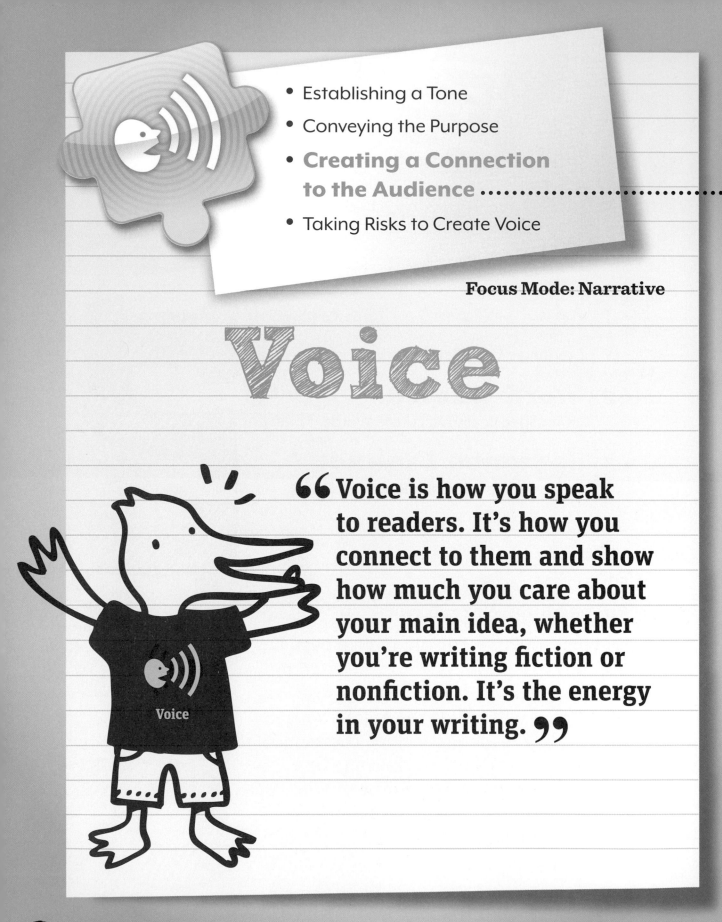

Voice

❝Voice is how you speak to readers. It's how you connect to them and show how much you care about your main idea, whether you're writing fiction or nonfiction. It's the energy in your writing. ❞

Creating a Connection to the Audience

If you're having trouble choosing the right voice, think about who is going to read the piece when it's finished. Who is your audience? Use your voice to connect with readers so they want to listen to what you have to say. Tell them what you think and feel. Make them understand what matters to you!

How is the person you talk to on the phone like your audience for a piece of writing?

Let's Connect!

Part 1: Write an e-mail about a birthday party you *really* want to go to. First, name your audience ("To:"), then write your message.

To:

Subject: birthday party

Part 2: Write an e-mail about a funny or exciting event ("Subject:"). Be sure to use just the right tone for your audience ("To:").

To:

Subject:

Warm-Up 13

That cat has energy. This paragraph doesn't! Give it some voice!

How well does this paragraph connect to its audience?

When I was 7 years old, I got a cat for my birthday. She is friendly and very playful. She follows me around and sleeps on my bed.

Revise the paragraph here or on a separate sheet.

Think About

- Have I thought about the reader?
- Is the tone right for the audience?
- Have I shown what matters most to me in this piece?
- Will the reader know how I think and feel about the topic?

Preview

Jerdine Nolen, author of *Raising Dragons*

Work with a partner to answer three of the questions below.

1. As a child, Jerdine Nolen loved collecting words. Two of her favorite words were *cucumber* and *chutney*. What are two of your favorite words?

   _____

   _____

2. Jerdine Nolen says, "Writing ideas are around all the time. . . . Some of my funniest ideas come from things that may not be so funny, like doing the dishes." What gives you writing ideas?

   _____

   _____

3. Once you have a story idea, Jerdine Nolen says it's important to revise the piece to make it the best it can be. What do you think is the most important thing to do once you have a story idea?

   _____

   _____

4. Jerdine Nolen's motto is "Hold fast to your dreams as you would your balloons!" What do you think she means?

   _____

   _____

Write-On Sheet

[Focus on Punctuation]

Write a short dialogue between two or three people. Start new paragraphs in the correct places.

_____

_____

_____

_____

_____

_____

66 No tears in the writer, no tears in the reader. No surprise for the writer, no surprise for the reader. 99

–Robert Frost

[Dreaming Big]

Jerdine Nolen's motto is

"Hold fast to your dreams as you would your balloons!"

Dragons?! Do they eat ducks? I'm outta here...

What dreams did the narrator of *Raising Dragons* have?
Write one of her dreams in each balloon.

Narrator
in
Raising Dragons

Do you feel it's important to hold fast to your dreams?
Why or why not?

_____

_____

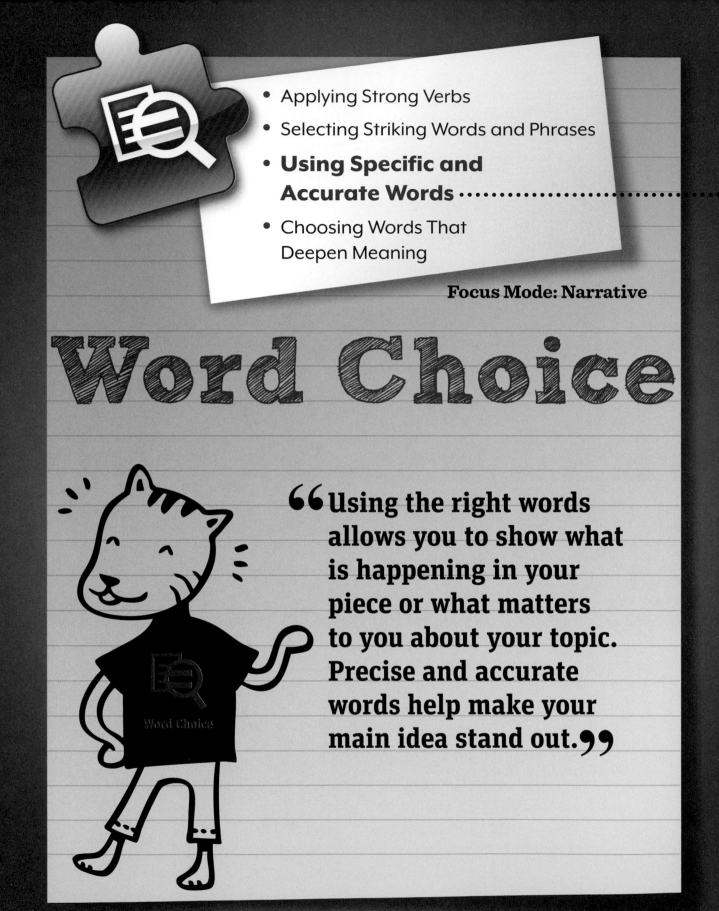

- Applying Strong Verbs
- Selecting Striking Words and Phrases
- **Using Specific and Accurate Words** ·······················
- Choosing Words That Deepen Meaning

Focus Mode: Narrative

Word Choice

"Using the right words allows you to show what is happening in your piece or what matters to you about your topic. Precise and accurate words help make your main idea stand out."

Using Specific and Accurate Words

Specific and accurate words give readers the information they need to understand your writing. For example, saying "The doctor helped the boy" doesn't grip a reader the way this does: "The pediatrician cured the boy of his terrible ear infection." Using words like these helps your reader see what you're trying to say.

Why is it important for both doctors and writers to use specific and accurate words?

Tell Me All About It

Write down all the details you remember about the objects you studied in class. Remember to use specific and accurate words.

Object 1:	Object 2:
Details I observed:	Details I observed:

Warm-Up 14

Does this paragraph contain specific and accurate words?

I have a best friend. He is so fun to be with. We do lots of stuff together. We like to see movies. We always see good ones.

Revise the paragraph here or on a separate sheet.

> The writer chose a best friend. Too bad he didn't choose better words!

Think About

- Have I used nouns and modifiers that help the reader see a picture?
- Did I avoid using words that might confuse the reader?
- Did I try a new word and, if so, check to make sure I used it correctly?
- Are these the best words that I could use?

Preview

A Television Scriptwriter

In the spaces below, fill in your thoughts about the job of a television scriptwriter.

1. What I think a television scriptwriter does:

_____

_____

_____

_____

2. The part of the job that I think would be most challenging:

_____

_____

_____

_____

3. My favorite TV show and what I like about the way it is written:

_____

_____

_____

_____

Write-On Sheet

[My Spelling Words]

List your nine spelling words for the week here.

1.
2.
3.
4.
5.
6.
7.
8.
9.

" Use the right word and not its second cousin. "

–Mark Twain

[The Greatest TV Show Ever]

Congratulations! You have been chosen to create a kids' TV show. Below, write the show's title, the names of its main characters, and its story line—what it's about.

Show Title: _____

Main Characters: _____

_____

Story Line:

_____

_____

_____

_____

_____

Write the first few lines of the script for episode #1. Remember to use specific and accurate words.

Pack your bags. You're going to Hollywood, baby!

_____

_____

_____

_____

_____

_____

- Crafting Well-Built Sentences
- Varying Sentence Types
- **Capturing Smooth and Rhythmic Flow** ·······················
- Breaking the "Rules" to Create Fluency

Focus Mode: Narrative

Sentence Fluency

❝To create sentence fluency, you have to read with your ears *and* eyes. Make your writing sound as good as it looks by building sentences that flow smoothly from one to the next. ❞

Sentence Fluency

Capturing Smooth and Rhythmic Flow

When you capture smooth and rhythmic flow in your writing, you turn tired, awkward sentences into fresh, natural-sounding ones. You bring a musical quality to your piece by varying the lengths of your sentences, starting them in different ways, picking just-right words, and using transitions to keep your message moving along and sounding sweet.

How is a fluent piece of writing like a song that makes you tap your toes to its rhythm?

Tricky Twisties

Don't let this twister tangle your tongue!

> How much wood would a woodchuck chuck
> if a woodchuck could chuck wood?
> He would chuck, he would, as much as he could,
> and chuck as much as a woodchuck would
> if a woodchuck could chuck wood.
> Yes, he would!

How many words are there in each sentence?	sentence 1: _____ words sentence 2: _____ words sentence 3: _____ words
What kinds of sentences are in the tongue twister? (statement, question, command, exclamation)	sentence 1: _____ sentence 2: _____ sentence 3: _____
What are the first three words in each sentence? Underline them above and write them here.	sentence 1: _____ sentence 2: _____ sentence 3: _____
What are some examples of alliteration?	

Write your own tongue twister that rocks.

_____

_____

Warm-Up 15

Oh, no—the flow is slow. Make it go!

How well does this paragraph flow?

I was afraid of the dark when I was little. I jumped at every sound. I hid under the covers. I hid in the closet too. I waited for morning.

Revise the paragraph here or on a separate sheet.

Think About

- Is it easy to read the entire piece aloud?
- Do my sentences flow, one to the next?
- Do individual passages sound smooth when I read them aloud?
- Did I place different sentence types thoughtfully in a way that enhances the main idea?

Preview

Gary Soto, author of *If the Shoe Fits*

Work with a partner to answer at least two of the questions below.

1. Gary Soto writes about growing up in the *barrio,* his Hispanic neighborhood. He uses details about people, foods, and daily life in the community. If you were writing about your neighborhood, what three specific details would you include?

_____

_____

_____

2. Gary Soto writes about experiences most kids have, like having a cookout or being stung by a bee. Choose an experience you've had and explain why it's one that you'd like to write about.

_____

_____

_____

3. Gary Soto writes poems as well as stories. Which traits do you think help him most to write poetry and to write stories that sound so smooth they are poetic?

_____

_____

_____

Write-On Sheet

[Focus on Grammar and Usage]

Write two sentences, one that contains a singular pronoun and one that contains a plural pronoun.

1. _____

   _____

2. _____

   _____

> 66 Writing isn't just on the page; it's voices in the reader's head. Read what you write out loud to someone—anyone—and you will catch all kinds of things. 99
>
> –Donna Jo Napoli

[Listen to the Flow]

Part 1: Listen to your teacher read aloud *If the Shoe Fits.*
Then answer the questions about Gary Soto's writing style.

Is the story pleasing to listen to?   Yes   No

Do the sentences flow and sound good?   Yes   No

Do all the sentences sound alike?   Yes   No

Do you hear different sentence types?   Yes   No

Does Gary Soto use carefully chosen words?   Yes   No

Part 2: Write a paragraph about a pair of magic shoes,
boots, or sneakers. Make the sentences flow smoothly.

You're taking a BIG "step" to becoming a great writer!

[Narrative Publishing Checklist]

Think you are ready to go public with your narrative project? Use this form to make sure you've covered all the writing bases.

I remembered to

☐ develop a fascinating story line with interesting characters.

☐ include time and place that work well with the story line.

☐ present a problem and solution.

☐ tell the story chronologically.

☐ use an active voice to entertain, surprise, and challenge the reader.

☐ choose words that enhance the characters, time, and place.

☐ read my piece aloud to check for how it will sound to the reader.

☐ proofread my piece carefully and clean up problems with conventions.

I'm not horsing around. Your narrative is superlative!

Conventions

The purpose of my piece is

_____

My favorite part is

_____

What I hope readers will find most memorable about my piece is

_____

Focus Mode: Persuasive

Whether you're asking your parents to let you stay overnight at a friend's house or convincing your teacher to get a class pet, the main purpose of persuasive writing is to construct an argument. You need to offer good, sound reasoning and use a strong, confident voice to let your reader know you mean business

- Finding a Topic
- Focusing the Topic
- Developing the Topic
- **Using Details** ....

Focus Mode: Persuasive

Ideas

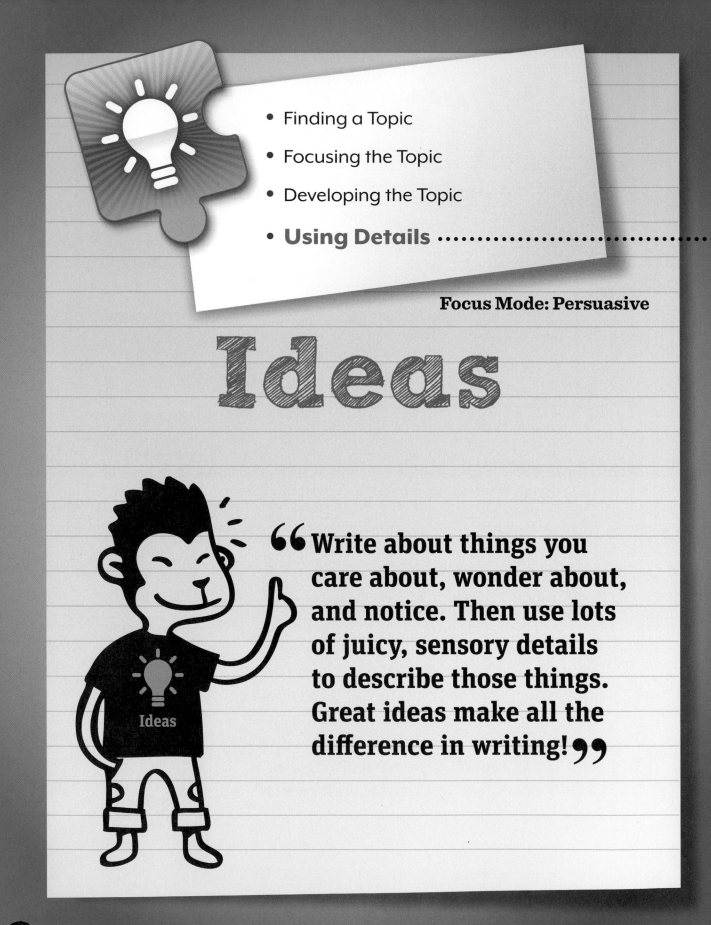

"Write about things you care about, wonder about, and notice. Then use lots of juicy, sensory details to describe those things. Great ideas make all the difference in writing!"

Using Details

When you write, you want your readers to see exactly what you are thinking. Details help readers imagine how something looks, feels, smells, sounds, or tastes. They make your ideas clearer and easier to understand. Your piece becomes a feast for the senses.

What is the connection between using your five senses in real life and using details in writing?

 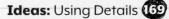

Show Me

Fill in sensory details to describe a delicious ice cream sundae.

How It Looks	How It Tastes	How It Smells	How It Feels in Your Mouth	How It Sounds When You Eat It
towering	sweet	chocolatey	smooth	slurp

Use your words to turn the following sentences that "tell" into sentences that "show."

Sentence that tells: The ice cream sundae was big.
Sentence that shows: _____
_____
_____

Sentence that tells: The ice cream sundae was good.
Sentence that shows: _____
_____
_____

Sentence that tells: Everybody liked it.
Sentence that shows: _____
_____
_____

Warm-Up 16

Who, me? I didn't drop those banana peels.

How are the details in this paragraph?

It's everyone's job to keep the lunchroom clean.
Yesterday I sat in something gross. What a mess!
Make sure you clean up your stuff.

Revise the paragraph here or on a separate sheet.

Think About

- Did I create a picture in the reader's mind?
- Did I use details that draw upon the five senses (sight, touch, taste, smell, hearing)?
- Do my details stay on the main topic?
- Did I stretch for details beyond the obvious?

Preview

Seymour Simon, author of *Penguins*

Work with a partner to answer at least two of the questions below.

1. Seymour Simon has written more than 250 books for kids about science. Some of his topics are penguins, paper airplanes, and planets. What's a nonfiction topic you'd like to write about?

   _____

   _____

2. Simon was an elementary school science teacher for many years. Do you think being a teacher helped him become a good writer? How so?

   _____

   _____

3. Seymour Simon grew up where there were many vacant lots. He got interested in the insects and plants there. Later, he wrote a book called *Science in a Vacant Lot*. What is something in your environment that gives you ideas for writing?

   _____

   _____

   _____

4. What is a question you would like to ask Seymour Simon?

   _____

   _____

   _____

Write-On Sheet

[My Spelling Words]

List your nine spelling words for the week here.

1.
2.
3.
4.
5.
6.
7.
8.
9.

❝It's the little details that are vital. Little things make big things happen.❞

–John Wooden

[What's the Cause? What's the Effect?]

Cause: Tasty fish in my pocket smells good.

Use the details in *Penguins* to complete the chart.

Cause		Effect
	→	There are only a few thousand Galápagos penguins left.

Cause		Effect
pollution in the ocean water	→	

Cause		Effect
development of coastlines	→	

Effect: Hungry penguin arrives.

- Creating the Lead
- Using Sequence Words and Transition Words
- Structuring the Body
- **Ending With a Sense of Resolution** ....

Focus Mode: Persuasive

Organization

"Organization is about the structure of a piece of writing. Nothing holds your piece together—or holds a reader's attention—better than sturdy, easy-to-follow organization."

Ending With a Sense of Resolution

The conclusion is the final touch on a piece of writing—its last lines. A good conclusion ties up all the loose ends and makes your piece feel complete. It's your last word, so be sure to give your readers something they will remember.

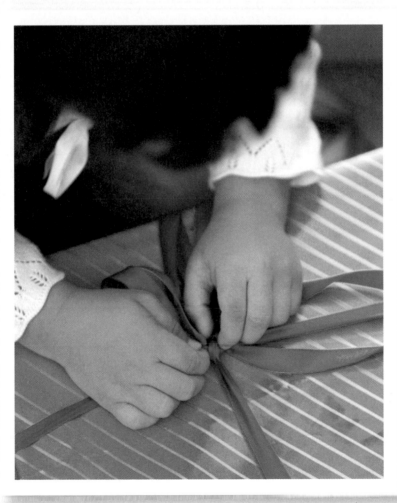

How is writing a strong conclusion like tying the ribbon on a gift?

Wrap It Up!

Here are some techniques writers use to end their pieces.

Technique	Example
A Question to the Reader	What would <u>you</u> do if you found a lost wallet?
A Challenge	Do the right thing. Turn in things you find that don't belong to you. You never know what they might mean to someone else.
A Quote	I just thought of what Mom always said. "Do the right thing, even if there's no one there to see you."
A Laugh	I knew Mom was proud. She patted me on the back. Then she said, "Now, if you could just find some of your missing socks!"
An Important Thought	When you do something good for others, you do something good for yourself, too.
A Strong Opinion	A person who does the right thing is a person I know I can trust.

Now use one of the techniques to wrap up this paragraph.

Doing the right thing is a small way to make the world a better place. I learned this when Mom helped me return a wallet I found that was full of money. The owner was so grateful.

_____

_____

_____

_____

Warm-Up 17

How is this paragraph's conclusion?

I wasn't happy about working in the park and picking up garbage. I didn't want to, but it was okay. That is all I have to say about my day cleaning up the park.

Revise the paragraph here or on a separate sheet.

I have something in common with the trees in the park: bark!

Organization

Think About

• Have I wrapped up all the loose ends?

• Have I ended at the best place?

• Do I have an ending that makes my writing feel finished?

• Did I leave the reader with something to think about?

Preview

A Movie Reviewer

Work with a partner to answer these questions about the job of a movie reviewer.

1. Many people think a movie reviewer's job sounds really fun. They get to watch movies for free! What do you think a movie reviewer would say is one part about the job that is not so great?

_____

_____

_____

_____

2. Where are places you might find reviews of movies?

_____

_____

_____

_____

3. Do you read reviews of movies before you go see them? How else do you get information about movies so you can decide whether or not you should go?

_____

_____

_____

_____

Write-On Sheet

[Focus on Grammar and Usage]

Write two sentences that contain correct use of homophone pairs.

1. _____

_____

_____

2. _____

_____

_____

66 Great is the art of beginning, but greater is the art of ending. 99

–Henry Wadsworth Longfellow

[Thumbs Up or Thumbs Down?]

Write in the chart the names of three movies you have seen. Check "thumbs up" if you liked it, "thumbs down" if you didn't.

What?
No popcorn?!

Name of Movie	Thumbs Up 👍	Thumbs Down 👎
1.		
2.		
3.		

Choose one movie and write a review. Give your readers something to think about at the end.

_____

_____

_____

_____

_____

_____

_____

- Establishing a Tone
- Conveying the Purpose
- Creating a Connection to the Audience
- **Taking Risks to Create Voice** ••••••••••••••••••••

Focus Mode: Persuasive

Voice

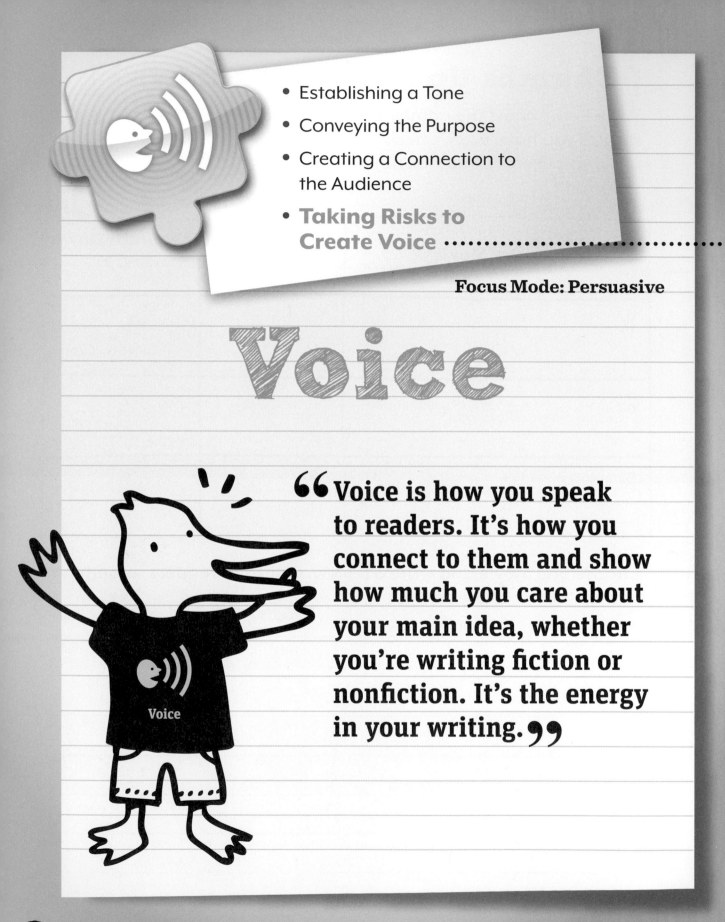

66 Voice is how you speak to readers. It's how you connect to them and show how much you care about your main idea, whether you're writing fiction or nonfiction. It's the energy in your writing. 99

Taking Risks to Create Voice

The best writers take risks. They might put a twist on a word to make it new or write in a voice they've never used before. If you want your writing to make a splash, you can't be afraid to take chances and try new things. Surprise your readers. In the process, you might surprise yourself!

How is taking risks in writing like parachuting from a plane?

Speak Up!

Picture this. A boy is watching TV in the living room with his dog, Rex, and his cat, Midnight. Oops! The boy spills his juice on the rug. He knows he's going to be in trouble, because he's not supposed to have food in the living room. The cat and dog look at each other. Here's what they're thinking.

Rex

I didn't make that spot on the rug, but I know I'll get blamed. I *always* get blamed. Just because I'm big and slobbery, doesn't mean I make messes. At least I don't throw up fur balls like other pets I know. I'm really in a *ruff-ruff-ruff* spot!

Midnight

Hee, hee, hee! Rex is going to be in trouble again. That big clumsy goofball gets blamed for everything. But everyone knows I'm the *purrfect* pet! Maybe I'll get some extra milk in my dish tonight.

Now it's your turn to take a risk and write from the point of view of one of the pets. If you choose Rex, persuade Mom or Dad you didn't make the spot on the rug. If you choose Midnight, convince Mom or Dad that he did.

_____

_____

_____

_____

_____

_____

Warm-Up 18

Did the writer of this paragraph take any risks?

Earth is getting warm. Everyone should do something. I walk to school. I think I am doing something good.

Revise the paragraph here or on a separate sheet.

> Walk? Doesn't anyone waddle anymore?

Think About

- Have I used words that are not ordinary?
- Is my writing interesting, fresh, and original?
- Have I tried to make my writing sound like *me*?
- Have I tried something different from what I've done before?

Preview

Patrick Jennings, author of *Guinea Dog*

With a partner, answer three of the questions below.

1. This author hopes to inspire students to take up their "magic wands," meaning their pencils. Do you think a writer's pencil is a "magic wand"? Why or why not?

_____

_____

2. When Patrick Jennings was a boy, he borrowed lots of books from the library. But he only finished the ones he couldn't stop reading. What kinds of books can you not stop reading?

_____

_____

3. Patrick Jennings was once a teacher and a librarian. How do you think that helped him become a good writer?

_____

_____

4. Patrick Jennings wrote *We Can't All Be Rattlesnakes* and *Faith and the Electric Dogs*. In one book, the narrator is a street dog. In the other book, the narrator is a rattlesnake. What does this tell you about Patrick Jennings's willingness to take risks to create voice?

_____

_____

Write-On Sheet

[My Spelling Words]

List your nine spelling words for the week here.

1.
2.
3.
4.
5.
6.
7.
8.
9.

" Push yourself to try new things—it will make you a better writer. "

—Deborah Nourse Lattimore

[Rufus Gives Reasons]

Imagine you are Rufus from *Guinea Dog*.
Write the reasons you should be allowed to
have a dog. Take risks to create voice.

Help Rufus get that dog! Give him a voice!

Here's Why I <u>Should</u> Have a Dog

_____

_____

_____

_____

_____

_____

_____

_____

_____

_____

_____

_____

[Persuasive Publishing Checklist]

Think you are ready to go public with your extended persuasive project? Use this form to make sure you've covered all the writing bases.

Check. Check. Ack. Check. I'm convinced!

I remembered to

☐ state my position on the topic clearly and stick with it.

☐ offer good, sound reasoning that the reader can relate to.

☐ provide solid facts, opinions, and examples that are based on reliable, objective sources.

☐ develop my argument using solid reasoning from beginning to end.

☐ use a compelling, confident voice to add credibility.

☐ explain any unusual words, phrases, or concepts.

☐ read my piece aloud to check how it will sound to my reader.

☐ proofread my piece carefully and clean up problems with conventions.

The purpose of my piece is

_____

The most critical point I make is

_____

What I hope readers will take away from my piece is

_____

Focus Mode: Expository

Whether your topic is Puerto Rico, pythons, or panning for gold, the main purpose of expository writing is to inform or explain. That said, your piece does not need to be a list of facts. In reality, it shouldn't be. Think about including fascinating details, intriguing insights, and life experiences. Good expository writing is written in a strong, confident voice—a voice that tells the reader that you know what you're talking about.

- Applying Strong Verbs
- Selecting Striking Words and Phrases
- Using Specific and Accurate Words
- **Choosing Words That Deepen Meaning** ....

Focus Mode: Expository

Word Choice

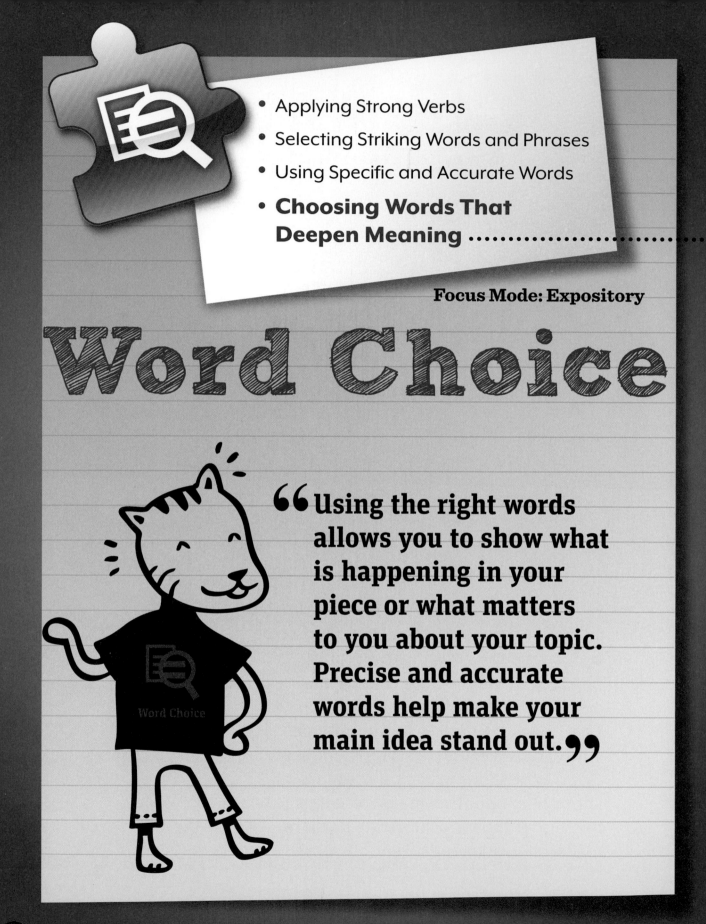

66 **Using the right words allows you to show what is happening in your piece or what matters to you about your topic. Precise and accurate words help make your main idea stand out.** 99

Choosing Words That Deepen Meaning

Good writers take their time. They stop to think about the best words to use—words that make their message clear. So, instead of using the first words that come to mind, dig deeper. Choose words that say exactly what you mean, paint pictures, and pack a punch. Give your readers something to think about.

How is coming up with a wish like choosing words that deepen meaning?

The Apple of My Eye

Read these words that are often associated with apples.

red	round	ripe	healthy
tree	pie	crunch	orchard

In the box below, write a fresh and juicy description of an apple—without using any of the words above.

Warm-Up 19

Hunt for food? Not me. I shop aisle 3 at the supermarket.

Do the words in this paragraph deepen its meaning?

If you're camping, you hear lots of sounds in the forest at night. You hear lots of different animals moving around. That's because many animals hunt for food at night. It can be a little scary.

Revise the paragraph here or on a separate sheet.

Think About

- Did I think carefully about the words I chose?
- Have I tried to avoid repeating words?
- Will my words capture the reader's imagination?
- Have I found the best way to express myself?

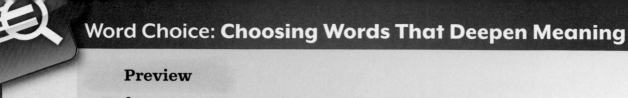

Preview

Dianna Hutts Aston, author of

An Orange in January

Work with a partner to answer three of the questions below.

1. As a child, Dianna Hutts Aston's favorite books were the Little House books and all of Beverly Cleary's works. Name three of your favorite books.

_____

_____

2. Aston likes a cozy, quiet space for writing, with pictures of her family on the walls. What's your idea of a perfect space for writing?

_____

3. On walks around her hometown, Aston noticed lots of birds' eggshells on the ground. That gave her an idea for a nonfiction book, *An Egg Is Quiet*. What is something that gave you an idea for a piece of writing?

_____

4. Aston's writing process goes something like this: First, she thinks. Then, she brainstorms. Next, she writes. Finally, she revises her work about 20 times and gets feedback from friends. Which of these things do you do, too?

_____

_____

5. Aston likes to write nonfiction about science topics like eggs and seeds. What nonfiction topics do you like to write about?

_____

_____

Write-On Sheet

[Focus on Conventions]

Write a sentence with correctly punctuated dialogue.

_____

_____

Write a sentence that contains correct use of two irregular plural nouns.

_____

_____

"As a writer, words are your paint. Use all the colors."

—Rhys Alexander

[Great Word Choices]

Write words and phrases from *An Orange in January* that capture your imagination. Tell why you like them.

Great Words and Phrases	Why I Like Them

Imagine that Dianna Hutts Aston adds a page to the book. What might she say about how the orange tasted to the boy? Use the best words you can.

C'mon. Squeeze out some great words!

_____

_____

_____

_____

- Crafting Well-Built Sentences
- Varying Sentence Types
- Capturing Smooth and Rhythmic Flow
- **Breaking the "Rules" to Create Fluency** ....

Focus Mode: Expository

Sentence Fluency

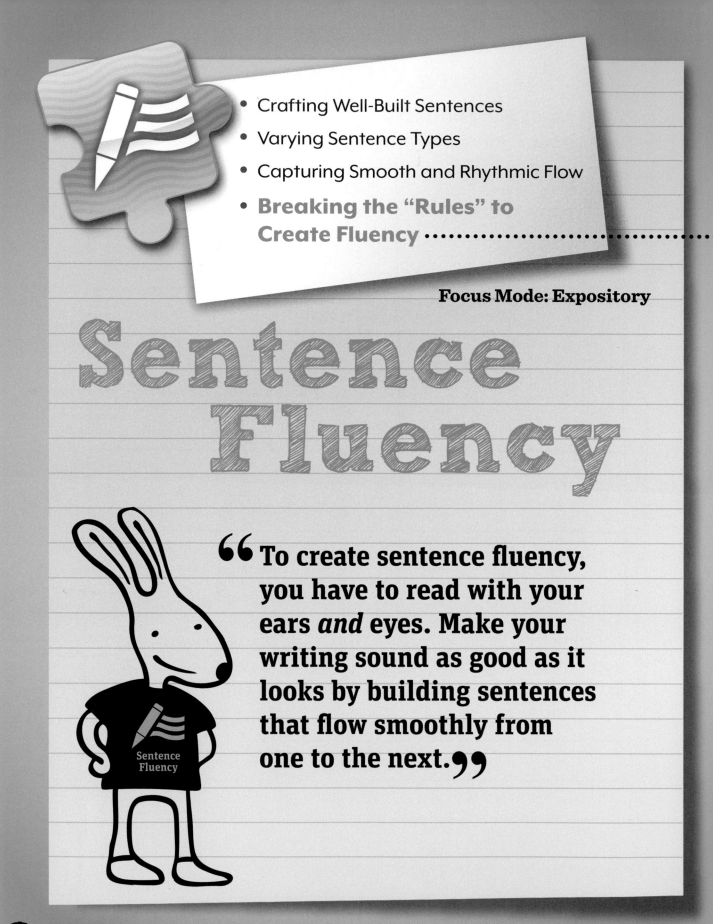

"To create sentence fluency, you have to read with your ears _and_ eyes. Make your writing sound as good as it looks by building sentences that flow smoothly from one to the next."

Sentence Fluency

Breaking the "Rules" to Create Fluency

You have learned many rules for writing sentences correctly. "Always include a subject and verb." "Don't start a sentence with a conjunction." "Never use one word as a sentence." But wait! To bring rhythm to your writing, you might need to break the rules or conventions sometimes. Interjections can highlight points. And sentence fragments can add style. Write it up. Light it up. Keep it flowing. Yes!

How is serving this unusual birthday "cake" like breaking the rules of writing?

Break It Up

Writers sometimes use incomplete sentences in their work. Here are some reasons they might choose to do that:

to emphasize a point	to give an example
Can you stop breathing? <u>Not for long!</u> She kept squirting water all over the place until the fire was out. <u>What a mess!</u>	And then there is the snow that begins to fall in fat, cheerful flakes while you are somewhere you'd rather not be. <u>Maybe school.</u> <u>Maybe work.</u>
to convey a sound	**to show excitement**
The honeybee is Louisiana's official state insect. <u>Buzz! Buzz!</u>	<u>Hurray!</u> I might get to go to the water park after all.

Pick a topic. Write a sentence and a fragment about it. Include an interjection, if you like. Then draw a picture about it.

Sentence: _____

_____

Fragment: _____

_____

Warm-Up 20

Did this writer break the rules to create fluency?

A desert is a dry place. It's really dry land and a bunch of sand. It has few plants. There are deserts in the southwest.

Revise the paragraph here or on a separate sheet.

Hmmm... sounds like a terrible place to grow carrots!

Think About

- Did I use fragments with style and purpose?
- Did I use informal language when it made sense to do so?
- Did I make dialogue sound authentic?
- Did I try weaving in exclamations and single words to add emphasis?

Preview

A Public Health Director

In the spaces below, fill in your thoughts about the job of a public health director.

1. Some kinds of things that I think a public health director is responsible for writing:

_____

_____

_____

_____

2. Where I have seen—or might be able to see—writing by a public health director:

_____

_____

_____

3. How a public health director's writings are like or unlike other kinds of everyday writing I've read so far:

_____

_____

_____

_____

Write-On Sheet

[Focus on Conventions]

Write a sentence that contains correct use of plural nouns.

1. _____

Write a sentence that correctly uses the verb *to be*.

2. _____

Write a sentence with correct punctuation of an abbreviation.

3. _____

_____

> " Following rules is not always the best way to write. Breaking the rules can result in better writing. Knowing when to break the rules and why is essential. "
>
> –Tom Aaron

[Make Them Laugh!]

Create a poster that explains five ways to make someone laugh.

If you know a good joke, I'm all ears!

Hee! Hee!

Ha-ha-ha!

Ha! Ha!

Hardy-har-har!

- Ideas
- Organization
- Voice
- Word Choice
- Sentence Fluency
- Conventions
- Presentation

Focus Mode: Expository

All Traits

> **The traits give you the language to talk about writing. You've learned a lot about the traits—what they are, how to look for them in your writing, and how to use them when you prewrite, draft, revise, and edit. What makes the traits so great? They help make YOU a great writer!**

Putting the Traits Together

All year, you have been breaking down your writing and looking at it trait by trait. Now it's time to look at all the traits at the same time— and see just how far you've come as a writer.

What do a jigsaw puzzle and a great piece of writing have in common?

Trait Savvy

Read this paper. Then read the Expert level in the Student-Friendly Scoring Guide for your assigned trait. Is the writer truly an expert? If so, underline the parts of the writing that prove it.

The Frog Leap

This is a true story about my babyhood. It was the year 2000 and I was ten months old. I was in my old house, the one I was born in. My Mom and Dad set me on my changing table and were standing right next to me. (That is the weirdest part!) I was being cute for them, giggling and drooling. My parents were admiring how darling I was and smiling. Just then, I did a frog leap right off the table, which really scared my parents! I bounced like a ball onto the water heater, which had a bunch of skinny ribs. Luckily the heater was not on and didn't burn me. When I was finished bouncing I just sat there. My Mom, Dad, and I all just stared at each other. Then we all started screaming! My Mom picked me up and we all went over to the couch for a Sonja sandwich hug.

Could some words and sentences be improved?
If so, circle them and revise them here.

_____

_____

_____

Warm-Up 21

How well does this writer use all the traits?

There are many kinds of bad weather like hurricanes, tornadoes, and blizzards. But if you're prepared, you'll be okay.

Revise the paragraph here or on a separate sheet.

C'mon cowboys and cowgirls—round up those traits!

Conventions

Think About

- Does my writing show that I understand my topic?
- Are my details in the best possible order?
- Can the reader tell I care about this idea?
- Have I painted a picture with words?
- Does my writing sound good when read aloud?

Juliana, Isabella, and Craig Hatkoff,

authors of *Winter's Tail*

With a partner, answer three of the questions below.

1. The Hatkoffs look to the news for their true stories about animals. Where else can you get ideas for true stories?

_____

_____

2. All three authors have to agree on which animal to write about. They have written about a baby hippo, a polar bear, a mountain gorilla, and a snow leopard. What baby animal do you hope they will write about in the future?

_____

_____

3. Craig Hatkoff sees that what humans do to the earth can cause problems for animals. What problem facing animals or our planet would you like to write about?

_____

_____

4. The authors believe that their stories can help protect our planet. Do you think writing can help the planet? Why?

_____

_____

Write-On Sheet

[Focus on Conventions]

Write a sentence that contains correct use of a singular or plural pronoun.

1. _____

Write a sentence that contains one correct pair of pronoun and contraction homophones.

2. _____

Write a sentence that contains a correctly capitalized proper noun.

3. _____

> " If there's a book you really want to read, but it hasn't been written yet, then you must write it. "
>
> –Toni Morrison

[Putting It Together]

The Hatkoffs are experts at Ideas, Organization, Voice, Word Choice, and Sentence Fluency. Write on the correct puzzle piece examples from *Winter's Tail* that prove it for each trait.

[Expository Publishing Checklist]

Think you are ready to go public with your expository unit project? Use this form to make sure you've covered all the writing bases.

Excellent job! You've definitely got the idea!

I remembered to

☐ include facts and information that came from reliable sources.

☐ weave in details that show how much I know about my topic.

☐ develop the topic logically from beginning to end.

☐ use a voice that expresses my fascination for the topic.

☐ explain any unusual words, phrases, or concepts.

☐ read my piece aloud to check how it will sound to my reader.

☐ proofread my piece carefully and clean up problems with conventions.

The purpose of my piece is

_____

The part that works best is

_____

What I hope readers will take away from my piece is

_____

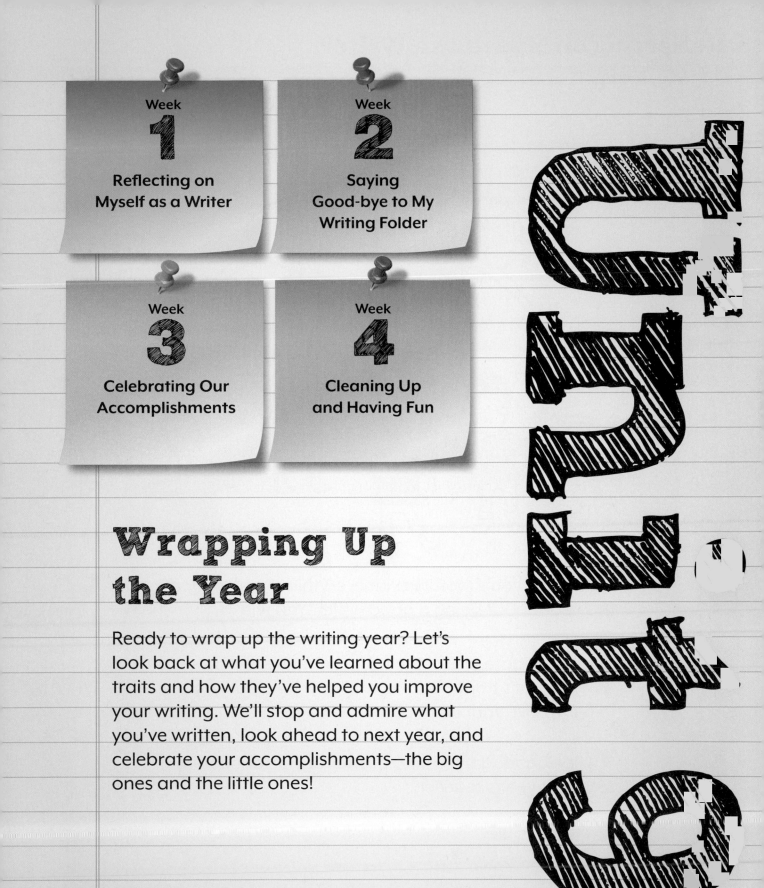

Week

1

Reflecting on
Myself as a Writer

Week

2

Saying
Good-bye to My
Writing Folder

Week

3

Celebrating Our
Accomplishments

Week

4

Cleaning Up
and Having Fun

Wrapping Up the Year

Ready to wrap up the writing year? Let's look back at what you've learned about the traits and how they've helped you improve your writing. We'll stop and admire what you've written, look ahead to next year, and celebrate your accomplishments—the big ones and the little ones!

Reflecting on Myself as a Writer

This week, you'll look back at everything you learned this year about being a good writer. You will

1 investigate one of the traits—what's easy about it, what's hard about it, and how it helped you improve your writing.

2 look ahead by writing a letter of introduction to next year's teacher.

This Trait Is Great!

Use this page to plan an oral presentation about your trait.

Trait: _____

Words to describe the trait:

_____

_____

_____

_____

Something the trait mate might say:

What's the most important thing to know about this trait: _____

_____

_____

Name an author who gets this trait really well and a book that proves it: _____

_____

A part of my writing that shows off this trait:

_____

_____

_____

[Oral Presentation Checklist]

Use this list to make sure you've covered all the bases for your trait presentation.

I remembered to

- [ ] list words that describe this trait.
- [ ] include something the trait mate might say.
- [ ] explain why this trait is important to good writing.
- [ ] name an author and a book that work particularly well in this trait.
- [ ] share an example of my writing that shows strength in this trait.

[Letter-Writing Checklist]

Use this list to help you decide what to say in your letter to next year's teacher.

I might mention

- [ ] what I'm really good at as a writer.
- [ ] the kind of writing I enjoy most.
- [ ] the name of my favorite trait.
- [ ] what I hope to get help with next year.
- [ ] a favorite book or magazine from this year.
- [ ] a question I have about next year.

Look at Me Now!

At the start of the year, you set goals for your writing (see page 11). Which goals do you think you've met— or surpassed—and which still need time and work?

_____

_____

_____

_____

_____

_____

_____

_____

_____

_____

_____

_____

Saying Good-bye to My Writing Folder

You've improved so much! And I'm not monkeying around.

This week, you will think about all the writing you did this year. You planned, drafted, revised, edited, and published lots of work. Now you will

 reread a piece of your writing from the beginning of the year, write another paper on the same topic, and use the traits to notice improvements you've made as a writer.

 clean out your writing folder and create a set of how-to directions for next year's class.

How to Write a How-to

A how-to paper is a set of directions that explains how to do something. Common "how-tos" are how to put something together, how to cook something, how to do something like a sport or hobby, and how to give directions or read a map.

To write a how-to, use these guidelines:

1. Provide an attention-grabbing reason for needing the how-to.
2. List any supplies or materials that are needed.
3. Give at least three step-by-step directions that build, in order, one to the next.
4. Wrap up with an example or scenario that shows the how-to in action.

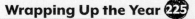

Saying Good-bye to My Writing Folder

Planning the How-to

Use this page to plan and draft your directions for how to use a writing folder.

Group members: _____

_____

Category assigned from class brainstorm:

_____

Attention-grabbing reason for folder:

_____

Supplies or materials: _____

_____

_____

Step 1: _____

Step 2: _____

Step 3: _____

Additional steps as needed: _____

_____

Wrap-up example or scenario showing the how-to in action: _____

_____

How to Use a Writing Folder

Category: _____

_____

_____

_____

_____

_____

_____

_____

_____

_____

_____

_____

Celebrating Our Accomplishments

Oh, yeah! Let's have some applause from my paws!

We celebrate holidays, special events, and now YOU, the writer! Yes, this week you and your classmates will continue wrapping up your writing year. Throw yourself into the fun activities your teacher has planned for you. This is guaranteed to be a week to remember!

Author, Author! Planner

Plan your letter to your favorite mentor text author. You will write your letter on another sheet of paper.

My Favorite Mentor Text Author:

_____

Title of the Author's Book:

_____

Why I admire how well the author handled the
_____ **trait.**

_____

_____

_____

_____

Things to do with the writer or the writing that I'd like to know more about:

_____

_____

_____

_____

Celebrating Our Accomplishments

Food Fair Planner

On the chart, write words associated with your trait and names of foods the words suggest. Then, create a menu.

My Group's Trait	Words that go with the trait	Foods that go with the trait
_____	_____	_____
	_____	_____
	_____	_____
	_____	_____

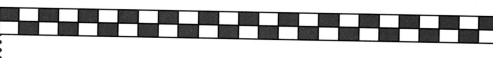

Menu for the _____ Trait

Writing Idol Voting Form

Listen carefully to the pieces that are read each day. Vote for the writers of the best ones.

Day 1: My choice for Writing Idol finalist is

_____

because _____

Day 2: My choice for Writing Idol finalist is

_____

because _____

Day 3: My choice for Writing Idol finalist is

_____

because _____

Day 4: My choice for Writing Idol finalist is

_____

because _____

Day 5: My choice for Writing Idol finalist is

_____

because _____

And the Writing Idol is . . .

Cleaning Up and Having Fun

Farewell from your furry, flappy, oh-so-fantastic friends!

This is it—our final writing week. You'll clean up your own space and help your teacher clean up the classroom. You'll also play some writing-related games. You may be surprised at how good you are at them after all the hard work you've put in as a writer. You've learned a lot—now it's time to have some fun and say so long.

Double Writing Puzzler

Unscramble each of the clue words. Write one letter in each box.

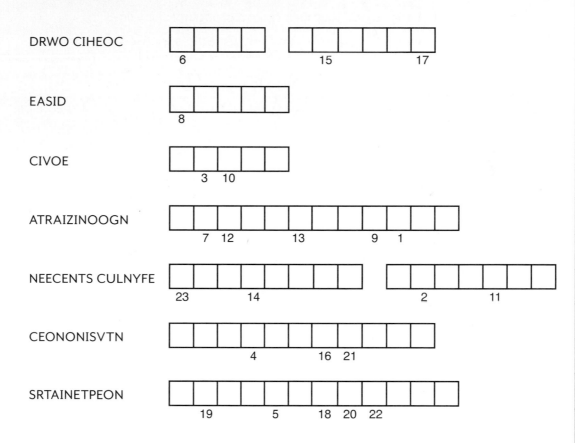

DRWO CIHEOC

⬜⬜⬜⬜ ⬜⬜⬜⬜⬜⬜
  6   15   17

EASID

⬜⬜⬜⬜⬜
8

CIVOE

⬜⬜⬜⬜⬜
  3 10

ATRAIZINOOGN

⬜⬜⬜⬜⬜⬜⬜⬜⬜⬜⬜⬜
  7 12   13   9 1

NEECENTS CULNYFE

⬜⬜⬜⬜⬜⬜⬜ ⬜⬜⬜⬜⬜⬜
23   14   2   11

CEONONISVTN

⬜⬜⬜⬜⬜⬜⬜⬜⬜⬜⬜
     4   16 21

SRTAINETPEON

⬜⬜⬜⬜⬜⬜⬜⬜⬜⬜⬜⬜
  19   5   18 20 22

Match each numbered letter above to a box below. Fill in the correct letters to spell out the sentence.

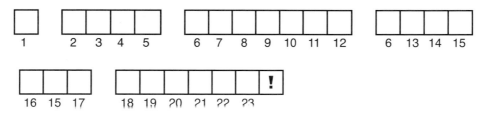

⬜ ⬜⬜⬜⬜ ⬜⬜⬜⬜⬜⬜⬜ ⬜⬜⬜⬜
1   2 3 4 5   6 7 8 9 10 11 12   6 13 14 15

⬜⬜⬜ ⬜⬜⬜⬜⬜⬜ !
16 15 17 18 19 20 21 22 23

Ideas

the content of your piece—its central message and the details that support that message

6 EXPERT

HIGH

My topic is well developed and focused. My piece contains specific, interesting, and accurate details, and new thinking about this topic.

- I have a clear central theme or a simple, original story line.
- I've narrowed my theme or story line to create a focused piece that is a pleasure to read.
- I've included original information to support my main idea.
- I've included specific, interesting, and accurate details that will create pictures in the reader's mind.

5 WELL DONE

4 ALMOST THERE

MIDDLE

My piece includes many general observations about the topic, but lacks focus and clear, accurate details. I need to elaborate.

- I've stayed on the topic, but my theme or story line is too broad.
- I haven't dug into the topic in a logical, focused way.
- My unique perspective on this topic is not coming through as clearly as it could.
- The reader may have questions after reading this piece because my details leave some questions unanswered.

3 MAKING STRIDES

2 ON MY WAY

LOW

I'm still thinking about the theme or story line for this piece. So far, I've only explored possibilities.

- I've jotted down some ideas for topics, but it's a hodgepodge.
- Nothing in particular stands out as important in my piece.
- I have not written much. I may have only restated the assignment.
- My details are thin and need to be checked for accuracy.

1 GETTING STARTED

Organization

the internal structure of your piece—the thread of logic, the pattern of meaning

6 EXPERT

HIGH

My details unfold in a logical order. The structure makes reading my piece a breeze.

- My beginning grabs the reader's attention.
- I've used sequence and transition words to guide the reader.
- All of my details fit together logically and move along smoothly.
- My ending gives the reader a sense of closure and something to think about.

5 WELL DONE

4 ALMOST THERE

MIDDLE

My piece's organization is pretty basic and predictable. I have the three essential ingredients, a beginning, middle, and end, but that's about it.

- My beginning is clear, but unoriginal. I've used a technique that writers use all too often.
- I've used simple sequence and transition words that stand out too much.
- Details need to be added or moved around to create a more logical flow of ideas.
- My ending needs work; it's pretty canned.

3 MAKING STRIDES

2 ON MY WAY

LOW

My piece doesn't make much sense because I haven't figured out a way to organize it. The details are jumbled together at this point.

- My beginning doesn't indicate where I'm going or why I'm going there.
- I have not grouped ideas or connected them using sequence and transition words.
- With no sense of order, it will be a challenge for the reader to sort out how the details relate.
- I haven't figured out how to end this piece.

1 GETTING STARTED

Voice

the tone of the piece—your personal stamp, which is achieved through an understanding of purpose and audience

6 EXPERT

HIGH

I've come up with my own "take" on the topic. I had my audience and purpose clearly in mind as I wrote and presented my ideas in an original way.

- My piece is expressive, which shows how much I care about my topic.
- The purpose for this piece is clear, and I've used a tone that suits that purpose.
- There is no doubt in my mind that the reader will understand how I think and feel about my topic.
- I've expressed myself in some new, original ways.

5 WELL DONE

4 ALMOST THERE

MIDDLE

My feelings about the topic come across as uninspired and predictable. The piece is not all that expressive, nor does it reveal a commitment to the topic.

- In a few places, my authentic voice comes through, but only in a few.
- My purpose for writing this piece is unclear to me, so the tone feels "off."
- I've made little effort to connect with the reader; I'm playing it safe.
- This piece sounds like lots of others on this topic. It's not very original.

3 MAKING STRIDES

2 ON MY WAY

LOW

I haven't thought at all about my purpose or audience for the piece and, therefore, my voice falls flat. I'm pretty indifferent to the topic and it shows.

- I've put no energy into this piece.
- My purpose for writing this piece is a mystery to me, so I'm casting about aimlessly.
- Since my topic isn't interesting to me, chances are my piece won't be interesting to the reader. I haven't thought about my audience.
- I have taken no risks. There is no evidence that I find this topic interesting or care about it at all.

1 GETTING STARTED

Word Choice

the vocabulary you use to convey meaning and enlighten the reader

6 EXPERT

HIGH

The words and phrases I've selected are accurate, specific, and natural-sounding. My piece conveys precisely what I want to say, because of my powerful vocabulary.

- My piece contains strong verbs that bring it alive.
- I stretched by using the perfect words and phrases to convey my ideas.
- I've used content words and phrases with accuracy and precision.
- I've picked the best words and phrases, not just the first ones that came to mind.

5 WELL DONE

4 ALMOST THERE

MIDDLE

My words and phrases make sense but aren't very accurate, specific, or natural-sounding. The reader won't have trouble understanding them. However, he or she may find them uninspiring.

- I've used passive voice. I should rethink passages that contain passive voice and add "action words."
- I haven't come up with extraordinary ways to say ordinary things.
- My content words and phrases are accurate but general. I might have overused jargon. I need to choose words that are more precise.
- I need to revise this piece by replacing its weak words and phrases with strong ones.

3 MAKING STRIDES

2 ON MY WAY

LOW

My words and phrases are so unclear the reader may wind up more confused than entertained, informed, or persuaded. I need to expand my vocabulary to improve this piece.

- My verbs are not strong. Passive voice permeates this piece.
- I've used bland words and phrases throughout—or the same words and phrases over and over.
- My content words are neither specific nor accurate enough to make the meaning clear.
- My words and phrases are not working; they distract the reader rather than guide him or her.

1 GETTING STARTED

Sentence Fluency

the way the text looks and sounds as it flows through your piece

6 EXPERT

HIGH

My piece is strong because I've written a variety of well-built sentences. I've woven those sentences together to create a smooth-sounding piece.

- I've constructed and connected my sentences for maximum impact.
- I've varied my sentence lengths and types—short and long, simple and complex.
- When I read my piece aloud, it is pleasing to my ear.
- I've broken grammar rules intentionally at points to create impact and interest.

5 WELL DONE

4 ALMOST THERE

MIDDLE

Although my sentences lack variety or creativity, most of them are grammatically correct. Some of them are smooth, while others are choppy and awkward.

- I've written solid shorter sentences. Now I need to try some longer ones.
- I've created different kinds of sentences, but the result is uneven.
- When I read my piece aloud, I stumble in a few places.
- Any sentences that break grammar rules are accidental and don't work well.

3 MAKING STRIDES

2 ON MY WAY

LOW

My sentences are choppy, incomplete, or rambling. I need to revise my piece extensively to make it more readable.

- Many of my sentences don't work because they're poorly constructed.
- I've used the same sentence lengths and types over and over again.
- When I read my piece aloud, I stumble in many places.
- If I've broken grammar rules, it's not for stylistic reasons—it's because I may not understand those rules.

1 GETTING STARTED

Conventions

the mechanical correctness of your piece, which helps guide the reader through the text

6 EXPERT

HIGH

My piece proves I can use a range of conventions with skill and creativity. It is ready for its intended audience.

- My spelling is strong. I've spelled all or nearly all the words accurately.
- I've used punctuation creatively and correctly and have begun new paragraphs in the right places.
- I've used capital letters correctly throughout my piece, even in tricky places.
- I've taken care to apply standard English grammar and usage.

5 WELL DONE

4 ALMOST THERE

MIDDLE

My writing still needs editing to correct problems in one or more conventions. I've stuck to the basics and haven't tried challenging conventions.

- I've misspelled words that I use all the time, as well as complex words that I don't use as often.
- My punctuation is basically strong, but I should review it one more time. I indented some of the paragraphs, but not all of them.
- I've correctly used capital letters in obvious places (such as the word *I*) but not in others.
- Even though my grammar and usage are not 100 percent correct, my audience should be able to read my piece.

3 MAKING STRIDES

2 ON MY WAY

LOW

The problems I'm having with conventions make this piece challenging to read, even for me! I've got lots of work to do before it's ready for its intended audience.

- Extensive spelling errors make my piece difficult to read and understand.
- I haven't punctuated or paragraphed the piece well, which makes it difficult for the reader to understand or enjoy my writing.
- My use of capital letters is so inconsistent it's distracting.
- I need to clean up the piece considerably in terms of grammar and usage.

1 GETTING STARTED

Presentation

the physical appearance of your piece—the welcome mat that invites the reader in

6 EXPERT

HIGH

My piece's appearance makes it easy to read and enjoy. I've taken care to ensure that it is pleasing to my reader's eye.

- I've written clearly and legibly. My letters, words, and the spaces between them are uniform.
- My choice of font style, size, and/or color makes my piece a breeze to read.
- My margins frame the text nicely. There are no tears, smudges, or cross-outs.
- Text features such as bulleted lists, charts, pictures, and headers are working well.

5 WELL DONE

4 ALMOST THERE

MIDDLE

My piece still looks like a draft. Many visual elements should be cleaned up and handled with more care.

- My handwriting is readable, but my letters and words and the spaces between them should be treated more consistently.
- My choice of font style, size, and/or color seems "off"—inappropriate for my intended audience.
- My margins are uneven. There are some tears, smudges, or cross-outs.
- I've handled simple text features well but am struggling with the more complex ones.

3 MAKING STRIDES

2 ON MY WAY

LOW

My piece is almost unreadable because of its appearance. It's not ready for anyone but me to read.

- My handwriting is so hard to read it creates a visual barrier.
- The font styles, sizes, and/or colors I've chosen are dizzying. They're not working.
- My margins are uneven or nonexistent, making the piece difficult to read.
- I haven't used text features well, even simple ones.

1 GETTING STARTED